S0-BRP-957

WILLIAM CHARLES MACREADY'S

King John

WILLIAM CHARLES MACREADY'S

King John

A facsimile prompt-book, edited by Charles H. Shattuck

University of Illinois Press, Urbana, 1962

Acknowledgments

No one can investigate any corner of the history of staged Shakespeare without returning again and again to the works of Professor Arthur Colby Sprague, whose pioneering book, *Shakespeare and the Actors,* first published in 1944, awakened the attention of theatre historians generally to the importance of prompt-books and acting editions as a well of information about the theatrical past. The older histories of William Winter and G. C. D. Odell, though less immediately in touch with these primary sources, remain also, of course, guides one cannot do without.

For immediately personal assistance I am indebted to more persons than I can remember — including Mrs. Lisa Puckle of Pirbright, Surrey, for making available to me the costume designs of Macready's *King John;* Mrs. Mary Reardon Keating, formerly of the Harvard Theatre Collection, Mr. George Nash of the Gabrielle Enthoven Collection, Mr. George Freedley of the New York Public Library, Mr. James McManaway and Miss Dorothy Mason of the Folger Shakespeare Library for generous assistance in research; Mr. Horace Groves of the Folger for expert photography; Miss Alma De Jordy, Miss Isabelle Grant, and Miss Helen Welch of the University of Illinois Library for aid in procurement of materials; Professor Alan S. Downer of Princeton University for invaluable advice; my colleagues Professors Edward Davidson, Gwynne Evans, Barnard Hewitt, and Wesley Swanson for critical assistance; the Graduate College Research Board of the University of Illinois for a study grant and for purchase of certain materials; the Board of the Folger Shakespeare Library for a Fellowship to read in the magnificent prompt-book collection of that library. I am grateful to the Folger Board above all for kind permission to reproduce their property — the prompt-book and scenes of *King John* — in the following pages.

Charles H. Shattuck
University of Illinois
March 3, 1962

CONTENTS

Illustrations

INTRODUCTION

We have had nothing so great as the revival of *King John.* We have had no celebration of English History and English Poetry, so worthy of a National Theatre. . . . It is six years since we saw *King John,* with some seven ragged supernumeraries for the power of England, while that of France, headed by a king in boots *à la* Louis Quatorze, crawled about the stage with three. What a picture has taken the place of this! There is a line in the tragedy about the alchemist, the sun, which turns with splendour of his precious eye "the meagre cloddy earth to glittering gold." Art is such another alchemist: converting to richest use the meagre resources of the stage. The rude heroic forms of the English past; the gothic and chivalric grandeur of the Middle Age; the woes and wars of a barbarous but an earnest time, with its reckless splendour, its selfish cruelty, and its gloomy suffering: are in this revival realized. . . . The accoutrements are complete, from the helmet to the spur of each mailed warrior. Not a distinction is missed in the appointments. From citizen to baron, gentleman to knight, herald to man-at-arms, soldier to servant, priest to king, gradations are marked with picturesque exactness, to the eye and to the mind. The scenery has had the same attention. The council room, the field before and after battle, the fortifications of Angiers, the moated and embattled fortress of Northampton, the glitter of the Royal tent, the gloom of Swinstead Abbey; they have all the air of truth, the character of simple and strong fidelity. And above all, in every movement of the tragedy, there is Mind at work, without which wealth of material is nothing. The crowds on the stage are instinct with life and passion. Yielding to the impulse of their leaders, they rise to fierce activity or sink into grim repose. These sudden changes are the very picture of that age: its selfish insincerity, its rude devotion, its servile slavery. Men they are not, though with those gallant forms of men, they are machines of war.

— *The Examiner,* October 29, 1842

Thus, and much more, wrote the exuberant John Forster in celebration of Macready's revival of *King John,* which had taken place at Drury Lane Theatre on October 24, 1842. Forster was a close friend of Macready's and an avidly partisan witness, but even so it is not amiss to take these glowing words of his for epigraph: every responsible critic in London paid homage to the production as "a great work," "glorious pageantry," "a careful and judicious study," "a work to be proud of," "an embodied picture . . . at once instructive and imaginative" which Shakespeare himself (if he could come back) would "applaud like a father." In after years, Charles Cowden Clarke used to round off his lecture on *King John* by likening Macready as a producer to Alexander the Great, who "placed the poems of Homer in a jewelled casket of inestimable price, the shrine being an emblem only of the offering" (*Shakespeare-Characters,* 1863, p. 342).

We may discount Clarke's metaphor as a flourish of platform eloquence; the reviewer's presumption of Shakespeare's "fatherly" response we recognize as a common Victorian sentimentalization. Yet unquestionably Macready's production of *King John* was magnificent. If, for some of the witnesses, it left something to be desired in the acting of the individual roles, that is not surprising, for the art of acting is the "impossible" art. But taken as a whole — the arrangement of the text, the ensemble playing, the stage decoration, the stage management, and the overall conception — *King John* was, together with the *As You Like It* which had opened the season three weeks earlier, the finest work that Macready had ever put together. This is to say that it was the finest which the Victorian "pictorial illustrating" age had yet seen. It was also an extremely influential production, as can now be demonstrated, providing the text and the stage business and affecting the stage decoration of all the important *King Johns* of at least the next two decades. Through the published "acting versions," it extended its influence much further: Robert Mantell, for instance, was still using "Macready's" book of the play as late as 1909.

Unfortunately for Macready's reputation, however, his production of *King John* has never been adequately described, and his influence upon the stage history of the play is almost wholly unrecognized. His own biographers — William Archer in 1890 and J. C. Trewin in 1955 — confine their remarks to some dozen lines of surface generalization or random detail, with a shred of testimony from some contemporary reviewer. The historians of Shakespeare in the theatre — William Winter (*Shakespeare on the Stage,* third series, 1916), H. H. Furness, Jr. (*The New Variorum Edition* of *King John,* 1919), Professor G. C. D. Odell (*Shakespeare from Betterton to Irving,* 1920), and Professor A. C. Sprague (*Shakespeare and the Actors,* 1944, 1948; and *The Stage Business in Shakespeare's Plays: A Postscript,* 1954) — report what they know from playbills and randomly collected reviews or from isolated acting versions or prompt-books; but none of these provides a satisfactory account of Macready's work, and every one of them falls into the trap of crediting to Charles Kean or Samuel Phelps ideas which these later producers simply appropriated from Macready.

The "Kean trap" was laid long, long ago, and very cunningly, by J. W. Cole — Kean's manager, publicist, and close friend — who in 1859, at the time of Kean's retirement from management of the Princess's Theatre, published his two-volume *Life and Theatrical Times of Charles Kean.* Cole prefaces his account of Kean's 1852 production of *King John* with a blandly insidious paragraph about Kean's production principles (II, 26):

> This [*King John*] may be considered the new manager's first *great* attempt on the plan he has since carried out with such indomitable perseverance and triumphant success. He had long felt that, even by his most eminent predecessors, Shakespeare in many respects had been imperfectly illustrated. He had seen what earlier actors and managers had accomplished. He felt that steps had been taken in the right direction, and longed ardently to press farther on in the same path, to a more complete end. No longer fettered by restraining influences, and confident in the result, although previous experiments were attended by failure, he entered boldly on the enterprise. The result is before the public. It has worked a total revolution in the dramatic system by the establishment of new theories and the subversion of old ones. The time had at length arrived when a total purification of Shakespeare, with every accompaniment that refined knowledge, diligent research, and chronological accuracy could supply, was suited to the taste and temper of the age. . . .

What measure of truth or what measure of puffery lies in these generalizations about Kean's attitude toward his "most eminent predecessors," his working "a total revolution in the dramatic system," or his effecting "a total purification of Shakespeare" cannot be argued here. It is unfortunate, however, that Cole chose the occasion of Kean's *King John* to pronounce these generalizations, for it was perhaps the least "original" of Kean's many Shakespearean productions. He simply took over Macready's *King John* of the preceding decade — text, staging, and all — tinkered it slightly, and added some trimmings. But Cole's rhetoric is so persuasive that everyone quotes it, taking it for whole truth. Thus Professor Odell, swamped by it, could write that "from the date of this production, Kean was noted as the first really great producer of Shakespeare in anything like our modern sense" (*Shakespeare from Betterton to Irving,* II, 286). It is not unfair to Kean to suggest that at least at *this* point his reputation has been unduly inflated, and might well be relieved of some of its rhetoric.

But my purpose in this study is more than to arbitrate the rival claims of dead actors. It is to *reconstruct* Macready's 1842 production of *King John* at Drury Lane Theatre — insofar as it is possible to reconstruct a living event within the covers of a book — so that we can know again, almost exactly, what was said and done, heard and seen, upon that long-forgotten stage. Although the play of *King John* stands today far below the first rank of popular favorites in the Shakespearean canon, nonetheless it serves remarkably well as a text upon which to renew our knowledge of an intricate and lost art of stagecraft. It was not a *first* rank favorite in Macready's time either, and for that very reason — because it was not staled by common usage — it was peculiarly available to a creative producer like Macready to lavish his art upon in a great revival. One might as easily reconstruct Macready's *Othello* (a comparable mass of evidence is available), but it would not tell us so much. The fact is that *the* Drury Lane prompt-book of *Othello,* which is preserved at the Folger Shakespeare Library, bears the inscription "This book prompted Kemble — Macready — Siddons &c"; and leafing through it one finds that the "&c" covers Edwin Forrest, John Vandenhoff, Charles Kean, and perhaps Edmund Kean also. In other words, a production of *Othello* in those days might have been handsome or might have been shabby, but in the essentials of "the book" — the text and basic stage business — it would not stray far from the forms established by the histrionic tradition and community. The book of *Othello* was quite rigidly fixed, precisely because it was played so often and because every aspiring tragedian had to be ready on call to perform either of its leading roles. It was also fixed, one must note, in conformity with the *moral* tradition and community. The acting version of *Othello* was pitifully docked and corrupted, partly to protect the image of the "hero," and emphatically to minimize its sex references; and any actor so foolhardy as to have restored the "true text" would have been hounded out of the profession by his shocked audiences and fellow actors. A play like *King John,* however — not in every actor's repertory and certainly less "dangerous" — lent itself very well in Macready's hands to a new production, which "seldom but sumptuous, showed like a feast, and won by rareness such solemnity."

The evidence for Macready's *King John* is extraordinarily full. I present here in facsimile a significant transcript of Macready's final prompt-book: the copy prepared for Charles Kean in 1846 by George Ellis (formerly one of Macready's prompters) which Kean used for his first staging of the play in New York City. I have examined and here report the details of and relationships between six other relevant prompt-books: Macready's personal preparation copy, John Willmott's "working copy" of the 1842 production, copies prepared by George Ellis for Samuel Phelps and Hermann Vezin, John Moore's copy, and Charles Kean's final prompt-book. I report also the details of the three "acting editions" that found their way into print: those of the *Modern Standard Drama,* Kean's souvenir edition, and T. H. Lacy's *Acting Edition of Plays.* A dozen sheets of water-color costume designs for Macready's production have recently been discovered by Macready's granddaughter, Mrs. Lisa Puckle: these are analyzed and presented in photographs.

I have found in the Folger Shakespeare Library water colors of William Telbin's fourteen scene designs for the play, accompanied by "carpenter's notes" in the hand of George Ellis: reproductions of these are presented. For purposes of comparison, I have included the fourteen scene designs for Charles Kean's final London production (1858), which are also at the Folger. Out of these materials, together with the verbal accounts of reviewers and other witnesses, it is now possible with a fair degree of exactitude to show the whole progress and effect of the play upon the stage — and with a happy double vision, too, for we can imagine ourselves viewing the play beside the spectator in the stalls and, when the scene changes, in the wings or behind the lowered act drop with the stage manager and his carpenter crews.

The Prompt-Books and Acting Editions

1. *Macready's preparation copy,* 1842 (Library of the University of Illinois). This is a small interleaved volume made up from an edition of George Steevens' *Shakespeare,* printed by Thomas White in 1825. The pages are numbered from 295 to 395 of volume IV. The pages and interleaves (which are of wove paper) are trimmed to 4½ by 7⅛ inches and bound in brown boards with a leather backing stamped *King John.* The front cover is inscribed within, "W. C. Macready, Sept. 8th 1842." This volume contains Macready's prospective cuttings, scenic prescriptions, stage maps, stage directions, and call lists, written in brown ink in Macready's own hand. In his *Diaries* he records that he completed his work on it on July 16, 1842, while vacationing with his family at Eastbourne. Again on August 23 he "cast the play . . . and cut out parts." A number of corrections and additions, in a lighter brown ink and a rather cramped hand, appear to have been entered by Macready after the book was bound.

2. *Willmott's prompt-book,* 1842-43 (Folger Shakespeare Library). This is a larger interleaved volume made up from a Steevens edition printed by A. Wilson (n.d.). The pages are numbered from 213 to 302 of volume V. The pages measure 5⅛ by 8⅛ inches and the interleaves 5¼ by 8 inches. The interleaves are of laid paper, watermarked 1840. The book is hand-stitched into a flexible gray cardboard cover, ink-labeled "P. B./King John/1842." In it all the matter from Macready's preparation copy has been exactly transcribed by a professional copyist; and in the rough hand of John Willmott, Macready's chief prompter, are various notes, corrections, warning signals, timings, and the like. A penciled annotation of "Original prompt book" correctly designates it as the working prompt-book of the Drury Lane production: it is well soiled from use.

From this copy, we must surmise, Willmott's assistant, George Ellis, made a polished master copy for his own uses, as he did of *As You Like It* and other pieces in Macready's Drury Lane repertory. No such copy has come to light, but the common identity of three later *King John* prompt-books executed by Ellis — those of Phelps, Kean, and Vezin — renders this supposition inevitable.

This George Cressall Ellis, who plays a most significant role in the story, is one of those lost heroes of the world-behind-the-scenes. A man of modest talent, but intelligent, steadfast, and efficient, he devoted his life to the theatre for but modest rewards, and his final reward has been oblivion. Born in December, 1809, he seems to have "entered the profession" when a youth of fifteen — such is the implication of a farewell note he once wrote to Charles Kean (Folger Shakespeare Library). At what theatre and in what capacity (juvenile actor? callboy?) he first appeared I do not know, nor have I been able to trace his activities during the first decade and a half of his professional life. He emerges in the Drury Lane lists in the fall of 1842, at the beginning of what was to be Macready's last season of management, playing such small parts as Dennis in *As You Like It,* "Luca" in *Othello,* Essex in *King John,* and a plebeian in *Julius Caesar;* more importantly he served as assistant to John Willmott the prompter. After Macready's withdrawal, Ellis stayed on at Drury Lane for several seasons in the post of chief prompter, and having access to the stage library he made for himself a collection of perfected prompt-books, mainly derived from Macready's recent productions. Occasionally too he transcribed these for other actors: I have seen copies he made for Samuel Phelps, Edwin Forrest, Charles Kean, and Hermann Vezin, as well as numerous books of his own. The marvel of all his prompt-books is their extraordinary calligraphy — probably the most systematic and beautiful in the history of the English stage. By 1848 he moved to the Haymarket, to prompt and to act small parts for Benjamin Webster. From 1850 to 1859, throughout Charles Kean's management of the Princess's Theatre, he was Kean's stage manager. In 1851 and 1852 he wrote or shared in the writing of the Princess's Christmas pantomimes; but his major work was to coordinate, with tact and skill, the hundreds of actors, supers, carpenters, painters, and mechanics who wrought the wonders for which the Princess's Theatre was famous. Scattered through the Kean correspondence at the Folger Shakespeare Library are a number of graceful notes from Ellis in acknowledgment of gifts, increases of salary, and other favors with which Kean rewarded him. After Kean retired from the Princess's, Ellis stayed on as stage manager under the management of George Vining, apparently with increasing responsibilities. In 1864, for instance, he prepared and staged a cut-down version of *The Comedy of Errors* (in one act and twelve scenes) which was well enough thought of to be published. A pastime of his later years was the compiling of a beautiful production book of *The Beaux Stratagem* (Harvard Theatre Collection), incorporating all the traditional business of that play that he could discover. This was but a labor of love, for, as he explains, the play is of course too indelicate ever to be performed for a modern audience. Meanwhile, as an honorary adjunct to his professional activity, he had long been associated with the "Windsor Theatricals." In 1848, when Charles Kean was called upon to produce these annual dramatic revels at Windsor Castle for the pleasure of the Queen, he took Ellis with him as assistant director (and keeper of account books). Ellis took great pride in this office. "It gave me a 'status' in the profession, — at once enviable and distinguished," he told Kean, "which I could not, perhaps, have otherwise attained." The "Master Ellis," whose name and fee as callboy at Windsor he often entered in the account books, was apparently his first son, whose name was also George. In 1859 Ellis was made in effect the principal director at Windsor. The Queen had appointed William Bodham Donne, the Examiner of Plays, to the post, and Donne, having no qualifications for the work, got Ellis to do it for him. "As my first step in office," Donne wrote to Kean, "I engaged the services of your ex-stage manager Mr. George Ellis and am greatly pleased with his zeal and intelligence." The only professional reference in Ellis' tiny obituary notice in the *Times* is to the fact that "for many years" he had been director of theatricals for the Queen. He died at his home in Chelsea on June 23, 1875, being then in his sixty-sixth year, and is buried in London's Brompton cemetery.

3. *Samuel Phelps's prompt-book,* 1843-67 (Folger Shakespeare Library). In May, 1843, near the close of Macready's management of Drury Lane, George Ellis made up a faithful copy of the *King John* prompt-book for Samuel Phelps, who as Macready's principal supporting actor was then sustaining the role of Hubert. Phelps had this prompt-book bound in marbled boards and brown leather backing, labeled *King John* and "S. P. / T.R.D.L." The text is from a Steevens edition printed by C. Baldwin (n.d.). The pages are numbered 297 to 395 of volume IV, and measure 4⅞ by 7⅜ inches. The laid paper interleaves, watermarked 1840, measure 5¼ by 7⅞ inches. Ellis endorsed this book in three places: (1) on the page following the Dramatis Personae he wrote "George Steevens's Edition / The Private Property of / / T.R.D.L."; (2) at the head of Act I he wrote "Prompt Copy — S. Phelps Esq[r] / Cut, — marked, — and corrected, / as acted at the / Theatre Royal, Drury Lane / by Geo Ellis / Prom[r] / May,

1843"; (3) at the end of the book he wrote "Geo Ellis / T.R.D.L." In the first of these inscriptions Phelps wrote "Sam[l] Phelps" in the vacant space and later he inked over "T.R.D.L." so that it reads "T.R.S. Wells." In the second inscription he inked over "Drury Lane" so that it reads "Sadler's" and added the word "Wells" to the line. An interesting feature of this prompt-book is that at the beginning of it nine pages of interleaves are filled with beautifully detailed descriptions of the costumes of most of the male characters (but none of the women's). These notes are a later accretion. They are not in Ellis' hand, and some of the leaves, tipped in, are watermarked 1847. They are certainly not derived from Macready's costuming of the play, and probably do not describe Phelps's original costuming of it either. Phelps entered upon his eighteen-year-long career of management of the Sadler's Wells Theatre on May 27, 1844, and on September 30 he first produced *King John* there, playing it eighteen times during the season. From time to time he repeated it, as at Sadler's Wells in February, 1851, and at Drury Lane in the autumn of 1865, in 1866, and in 1867. I think he used the same prompt-book through all these years: the marbled surface of the cover boards is worn almost to a common gray and portions of the surface have been torn away by heavy handling. Phelps added here and there a few details of stage business, but for the most part he used Macready's text and directions intact. Here it must be noted that Professor Sprague's observations on Phelps's *King John* have gone awry from failure to observe the genetics of Phelps's prompt-book (*The Stage Business in Shakespeare's Plays*). He quotes from it seven interesting stage directions, and concludes that "Such directions as these . . . bear out one's belief that at Sadler's Wells there was not merely vigilance in matters of detail but spirited *ensemble* playing of a sort as yet unknown elsewhere in England." But every one of these directions had been written down by Macready in his preparation copy in the summer of 1842 and put into effect in the production at Drury Lane. They are all recorded in Willmott's prompt-book. Ellis had transcribed them for Phelps almost verbatim.

4. *John Moore's prompt-book,* c. 1843 (Folger Shakespeare Library). In the early 1840's a young Englishman (Irishman?) named John Moore, a prompter and minor actor with an eye to the future, began building a library of prompt-books taken from the best productions of the times. About 1848 he emigrated to America, where for the next forty years or more he was one of the most active (though now forgotten) workers behind the scenes of the New York stage. Moore's prompt-book style is as unprepossessing as George Ellis' is beautiful: his handwriting is often rough and crabbed, and his books are sometimes nearly impenetrable because of the layers upon layers of notes and observations he would take from the innumerable "stars" that crossed his stages. His transcription of Macready's *King John,* however, is reasonably clean and neat. The text pages are 193 to 290 of volume IV of a Steevens edition, and measure 5½ by 8 inches. The interleaves are 4¼ by 7¼ inches. The binding is of tan cardboard, with the title and Moore's signature inked on the cover. The transcription is somewhat simplified from the original, but the essentials are complete. The pages are so uncluttered and even unthumbed, compared to many of Moore's books, that I doubt he used it much, if ever, at the prompter's table.

5. THE PROMPT-BOOK HERE REPRODUCED. *Charles Kean's prompt-book,* New York, 1846 (Folger Shakespeare Library). Charles and Ellen Kean spent the seasons of 1845 to 1847 in America. On November 16, 1846, at New York City's Park Theatre, familiarly known as "Old Drury," they brought out a production of *King John* "on a scale of splendour," as J. W. Cole tells us (*The Life,* I, 344), "which no theatre in London or Paris could have surpassed. The scenery, the decorations, the banners, armorial bearings, heraldic blazonry, groupings, weapons of war, costumes, furniture, and all the minor details were so correctly studied that the most scrutinizing reader of Montfauçon or Meyrick would have been puzzled to detect an error." Cole of course does not mention the fact — perhaps, indeed, he did not know it, for he did not join the Keans professionally until the 1850's — that for this event

George Ellis provided Kean a copy of Macready's prompt-book and water colors of Macready's scene designs also. The prompt-book is in all essentials identical with the copy Ellis made for Phelps three years earlier, with the addition of only a few advices and exclamatory warning notes "to the Prompter!" The text pages are again from a Steevens edition, numbered 193 to 290 of volume IV and measuring 5½ by 8¾ inches. The interleaves are of sturdy wove paper, measuring 7⅛ by 8⅞ inches. Kean eventually had the book handsomely bound in marbled boards with black leather backing and corner tips filigreed with gold. The cover label is gold-stamped M[r] CHARLES KEAN. Ellis inscribed the book as follows: "Prompt Copy / Cut, — marked, — corrected, — &c. — &c / for Charles Kean, Esq[r] / by — George Ellis / prompter. / Theatre Royal, Drury Lane / March, 1846." There is no question that this is the book that Kean used, stage directions and all, for his New York production. The pages show signs of much handling, and there are throughout many notations by the New York prompter, including at the front of the book an act-by-act schedule of the playing time "at Park Theatre 1846" and at the back four more rough sets of timings. A few lines are cut and a few restored. In the first act the Bastard is several times newly directed to "Smile." Off-stage drums and trumpets are frequently redirected to sound "in Orchestra." Occasional lighting warnings are added. The sound cues are numbered, the final "Organ Music" being number 39. Just before the last scene there is a note to "Call Mrs. Kean," obviously to ready her for the curtain call. The only really major alteration occurs in IV.3, the scene of Arthur's leap from the tower, in which Kean reversed the weight of the scenery from stage left to stage right (as he also did in subsequent productions), so that all the "R's" and "L's" are transposed. I have elected the contents of this prompt-book for facsimile reproduction because it shows accurately enough the manner of Macready's staging of the play in 1842, and at the same time shows how Kean first staged it in 1846.

6. The acting version of the *Modern Standard Drama,* 1846 (later, no. XXXV of *French's Standard Drama*). A few days before the Keans opened *King John* at the Park Theatre, the firm of William Taylor and Company, 2 Astor House, published the acting version, "With the Stage Business, Cast of Characters, Costumes, Relative Positions, &c. / Also a List of Authorities for Costumes / BY CHARLES KEAN, ESQ. / As Produced with great Splendour at the Park Theatre." The book could be purchased separately for a shilling (American), or, together with the eight other plays that made up volume III of the *Modern Standard Drama,* for a dollar. The editor of the volume, himself a poet and dramatist, was Epes Sargent, who had initiated the *Modern Standard Drama* some three or four years earlier for the now defunct publishing firm of Mowatt and Company. In his "Editorial Introduction," Sargent was scrupulously specific and accurate in ascribing to Macready "the present judicious abridgement," and in crediting Macready for having "improved and rearranged the business" and having "introduced much that is novel in the externals of the scene, besides restoring many passages from the original text, which should never have been omitted." He claims to have studied the "contested readings" with care and occasionally to have exercised his own judgment as to which lines to print. "The present acting edition is the first ever published containing the new [Macready's] restorations and directions." By way of describing the Kean production, which was yet to be seen, Sargent printed a patchwork of reviews from two London journals, the *Spectator* and the *Examiner,* which describe Macready's 1842 production — assuring us that except in the point of "historical accuracy," in which Kean's production will be superior, the description will be "equally applicable to the style in which it is to be put upon the stage at the Park."

Sargent's ascription of the acting version to Macready should be clear enough and emphatic enough, but historians have uniformly disregarded it. William Winter, in reviewing Robert Mantell's production in 1909, refers to this edition only as "the old version authorized by Charles Kean" (*New York Tribune,* March 9, 1909). Throughout the *New Variorum Edition,* H. H. Furness, Jr., alludes to this edition as Kean's (pp. 28, 351, 661). Professor Odell neglects to mention it at all, presumably because as it was an American publication he assumed it irrelevant to his subject. In *Shakespeare and The Actors* (pp. 108-116) Professor Sprague calls it simply "a Charles Kean edition" and specifically credits to Kean nearly a dozen pieces of business which were invented by Macready.

7. *Charles Kean's souvenir edition,* 1858. During Kean's management of the Princess's Theatre in London, he revived *King John* twice — on February 9, 1852, and on October 18, 1858. For the second of these occasions he caused to be published a souvenir edition of the play ("Price One Shilling / To Be Had in the Theatre") — an eighty-four-page booklet nicely printed by the publishing firm of his brother-in-law, John K. Chapman. It is embellished by a Dramatis Personae, a Preface in which Kean underscores the historical accuracy of his costumes and scenes, explanatory footnotes on nearly every page, and at the end of each act two or three pages of "Historical Notes." The text of the dialogue, cut as Kean finally played it, differs but little from that of the *Modern Standard Drama*: a few more lines are deleted from the first act to minimize the adultery theme. But since this is an edition for spectators and readers, rather than for the profession — its intention being "to promote the educational purposes for which the stage is so pre-eminently adapted" and "to convey information to the general public through the medium of refined amusement" — all technicalities of stage direction except the barest necessities of entrances and exits, trumpet calls, alarums, marches, and the like are stripped away.

8. *Charles Kean's prompt-book,* 1859 (Folger Shakespeare Library). I have not seen a prompt-book specifically identified with Kean's 1852 production, but it is fair to assume that if one comes to light its text will not differ markedly from the prompt-book of 1846 or the souvenir edition of 1858. When Kean terminated his management of the Princess's Theatre in 1859 he caused his prompter T. W. Edmonds to make up for his library clean copies of the prompt-books of all his important productions. The book of *King John* is inscribed as follows: "Cut, marked and corrected / for Charles Kean Esq[r] / by T. W. Edmonds, Prompter / Royal Princess's Theatre, London / 1850 to 1859." The text pages, which measure 5¼ x 8 inches, are those of the souvenir edition. The interleaves, 6⅞ x 9 inches, are of undated laid paper. Edmonds' stage directions are practically all verbatim copies of George Ellis' originals. The book is bound, as are all the others which Edmonds made up at this time, in tan boards with light brown leather corner-tips and backing. The main point of interest is that each scene is accompanied by a water-color scene design. I shall revert to these designs in a later section of this study. (Another set of these designs, by the way, is preserved in the Gabrielle Enthoven Collection at the Victoria and Albert Museum. These are slightly larger and rather more handsomely colored than the Folger prompt-book set, but except for a few tiny details — a green rug leading to the throne in Act I, a small blue flag mounted on the war machine in Act II, a broken spear in the foreground of Act III.2. — they are essentially the same.)

9. *Hermann Vezin's prompt-book,* 1859 (?) (Library of the University of Illinois). Sometime in or after 1858 George Ellis made up a "perfect" copy of the Macready acting version for Hermann Vezin, as part of a set of at least nine prompt-books he executed for that actor. Ellis used the text pages of Kean's souvenir edition, but he carefully wrote in and struck out lines so as to restore Macready's exact text. On the interleaves, which are of undated laid paper measuring 7 1/4 by 9 1/16 inches, he meticulously transcribed all the stage directions from his own (hypothetical) master copy. *King John* was perhaps not a favorite role of Vezin's, but he is known to have played it during his management of the Surrey Theatre in the summer of 1859.

10. *Lacy's Acting Edition,* 1858 or 1859. Sometime in or after 1858 Thomas Hailes Lacy added *King John* to his *Acting Edition of Plays,* thus providing the theatrical profession in England with what the *Modern Standard Drama* had provided in America some

dozen years earlier. Lacy's theatrical and editorial affinities are problematic. The usual practice in printing cast lists in "acting editions" is to give the most recent one in full and to abbreviate those from the past. Lacy exactly reverses this procedure. He prints a *fairly* full cast list of Kean's 1858 production, a somewhat fuller cast list of Phelps's 1844 production (in which, by the way, Lacy himself played the French King), and a complete cast list of Macready's 1842 production. He does not describe the current (or forthcoming?) Kean production, but reproduces from the *Modern Standard Drama* the old patchwork description of Macready's production. He reprints Kean's 1846 "Authorities for the Costumes," but, he says, "with some corrections and additions by the editor." In short, he seems at once to be snubbing Kean and capitalizing on Kean's 1858 revival: a catch-penny device. His treatment of the text is curious, too. It is not a literal reprinting of the American acting edition (it adds forty-one lines and deletes sixteen); nor does it accurately reproduce the text of any prompt-book of the time that I have examined. For all that, however, it is still essentially a "Macready" version of the play. One can be sure that Lacy never laid eyes on the stage directions that Macready penned in his preparation copy at the seaside in 1842. These had been "edited" over the years as they were transcribed by George Ellis, by Epes Sargent, and by Lacy himself. Yet it is remarkable how in this last printing they correspond in idea, word, and phrase to what Macready had originally set down. Quotation at length would be otiose. Three brief examples will suffice. In I.1, Macready wrote: "As the King descends, Elinor advances a little towards Philip, and the Nobles approach the King as if speaking of the litigants." Lacy prints: "rises and descends. — Queen Elinor follows, and approaches Faulconbridge. — Some Nobles accost the King, as if referring to the litigants." In IV.1, Macready wrote: "Arthur, who has been playing with his bow, observing Hubert, flings it away, & goes to him." Lacy prints: "Arthur, who has been playing with his bow L., suddenly looks at Hubert intently, then goes to him." In V.1, Macready wrote: "John is giving his Crown to Pandulph, who places it on a cushion. John then places his hands between those of Pandulph, as doing homage. The Music of the Church is heard during the Ceremony." Lacy prints: "King John is in the act of giving his Crown to Pandulph, who places it on a cushion held by a Bishop. John kneeling then places his hands between those of Pandulph, as doing homage. Organ music is heard during the Ceremony." Such verbal correspondences might be multiplied many times over, and it can be said in general that all the distinctive stage business of Lacy's edition tallies with George Ellis' recording of the production of 1842.

Macready's Text

The text of *King John* had not been very seriously tampered with (except for cutting) during its stage history, as had *As You Like It,* for instance, so that Macready had neither the obligation nor the opportunity to "restore the true text." The earliest corruption of it, Colley Cibber's *Papal Tyranny in the Reign of King John,* had died aborning a hundred years earlier: kept off the stage by popular outcry in 1736, it was beaten when it finally did appear at Covent Garden in 1745 because of Garrick's shrewd maneuver of opposing it with a version of Shakespeare's own play at Drury Lane. The Reverend Richard Valpy's pious perversion of *King John* for the schoolboys at Reading in 1800 (and in 1803 for the public at Covent Garden!) was similarly superseded by John Kemble's restoration of the text of Shakespeare. Only two small batches of non-Shakespearean matter seem ever to have intruded into the regular acting versions. Garrick, following Pope's edition, borrowed a dozen lines from *The Troublesome Raigne of King John* which he inserted at III.1.63, and three more lines at III.2.8, to motivate the hostility of the Bastard toward the Duke of Austria. These lines were printed in Bell's edition in 1773; but by 1804 Kemble eliminated them. The Napoleonic crisis about the turn of the century stirred up a specious popularity for the play as a vehicle for Francophobia, and under the pressure of this national hysteria Kemble permitted the Bastard, at V.1.78, to utter the following jingoism (of unknown authorship):

> Sweep off these base invaders from the land:
> And above all, exterminate those slaves,
> Those British slaves, whose prostituted souls,
> Under French banners, move in vile rebellion,
> Against their king, their country, and their God.

This "base and hacknied claptrap," as J. W. Wallack once labeled it (in a prompt-book now in the Library of the University of Illinois), may be found in all Kemble editions, in Mrs. Inchbald's, and in Oxberry's, and it was the sole stain remaining on the text when Macready undertook his revision.

Macready's task was simply to establish a workable acting version, in his lights faithful to Shakespeare and suitable to his theatre and his audience. The original is 2,570 lines, too long in more senses than one for Macready's uses. Garrick's version, as represented in Bell's edition, was about 1,905 lines, not counting the non-Shakespearean bits. Kemble's version was slashed to about 1,690 lines. Macready, with the original before him and Kemble beside him, established a text of 1,830 lines. This, with minor additions and subtractions, passed into print, as we have seen, to become the standard acting version for the nineteenth century.

The first act presented Macready with a problem of decorum, for much of it consists of a bold exposition of the Faulconbridge family's case of adultery and bastardy. As the 1842 critic of the *Atlas* remarked, "To render Faulconbridge fit for 'ears (very) polite' is no slight difficulty." Garrick had produced nearly the whole language of the act without regard for moral niceties. The editor of Bell's edition, Francis Gentleman, objected to this, regretting among other things that Lady Faulconbridge was brought upon the stage "to criminate herself so indelicately"; but it had not occurred to Garrick to concede to such prudery. The Reverend Valpy got around the difficulty with his schoolboys by suppressing the first act entirely; and when Kemble restored the act pretty much as Garrick had played it, Valpy was scandalized "that the indecencies of the First Act should be tolerated . . . in this age of moral refinement, in the reign of a Prince, who displays an exemplary detestation of everything, that is not chaste in sentiment, and fine in expression" (Preface, Valpy's edition, 1803). By 1842 Macready had to reckon with a prudery which was nearly universal: he expunged about twenty-two lines in order to soften the rudeness of the scene, and he succeeded well enough, it appears, to assuage the sensibilities of the *Atlas* and other "ears polite." In Kean's souvenir edition of 1858, fourteen more lines were cut in deference to decorum.

In the second act Garrick retained rather more than enough of the rodomontade of the Kings John and Philip when they meet each other before Angiers, and reduced the invective between Elinor and Constance. Francis Gentleman objected caustically to the brawling of the kings, comparing their encounter to that of Prettyman and Volscius in *The Rehearsal,* "with this difference, that the burlesque Princes are rather more polite." Kemble cut down the kings' speeches by about fifteen lines, and Macready followed suit. Kemble restored some mouth-filling lines to the ladies and Macready gave them eight or ten more.

In many of the larger cuttings, Macready very often took Kemble's and/or Garrick's lead. In the first act, for instance, Faulconbridge's soliloquy (lines 182-219), which in Garrick's time was spoken entire ("somewhat tedious, and very obscure," Gentleman called it), had been reduced by Kemble from thirty-seven lines to seven. The stick figure of Blanch had long been relieved of most of her speeches, including her word-chopping acquiescence to marriage (II.1.510-520) and her static agony when the impending wars torture her loyalties (III.1.326-336). Pandulph's remarkable but not particularly stage-worthy display of casuistry (III.1.268-294) had been shorn of twenty-seven lines. Some of the typical "echo" passages, practiced so ardently by Shakespeare in his artistic nonage, in which a single word is dinged at us in line after line — the "sin" and "plague" lines (II.1.179-190) and the "law" lines (III.1.184-190) — had always been omitted. The frenetic conceit between Philip and Constance on the love that dwells among hairs ("ten thousand wiry friends / Do glue themselves in sociable grief," and so on, III.4.61-75) had been dispensed with by Kemble. The last scene in the French camp (V.5) had always been eliminated.

It might be said that Shakespeare himself recommended cutting the text of this play, and provided the motto and the example by which the cutting should be done. There is a famous passage in IV.2 in which Salisbury protests that

> To gild refined gold, to paint the lily
> To throw a perfume on the violet . . .
> Is wasteful and ridiculous excess.

Between the second and third of these lines Shakespeare violated the very point his speaker is making by pitching in three more (very pretty but "ridiculously excessive") demonstrations:

> To smooth the ice, or add another hue
> Unto the rainbow, or with taper-light
> To seek the beauteous eye of heaven to garnish.

In short, the play is often "too long" — or, as Francis Gentleman declared in his Introduction, "Prolixity seems to have been Shakespeare's study, in many scenes and speeches of this play." It was not difficult for Macready, having Kemble's expert practice before him, to cut 740 lines from the play without hurting its essential completeness and its dramatic potential. He was able, too, to restore over a hundred lines that Kemble had dropped. Constance and Pandulph gain back valuable lines in the early acts; John, the Bastard, Melun, and the English lords are given useful bits in the later acts. The figure of Peter of Pomfret returns to the stage in IV.2, and the fulfillment of his prophecy in V.1. And one is grateful to see restored such jewel-like lines as "How easy dost thou take all England up!" (IV.3.143) and "I am the cygnet to this pale faint swan" (V.7.21).

The Spectacle

The critics of the day took great delight in describing and praising the "spectacle" of *King John* — that is, the scenery, the costumes, and the stage grouping and movement; and many of them made the point that here was not spectacle for the sake of spectacle, but spectacle which fitly and splendidly subserved the meaning of the play. "We consider that Mr. Macready has displayed not only great knowledge and taste; but, what is more praiseworthy, great moderation, in the command of his resources," said the *Atlas*. "We have never witnessed a representation in which the 'getting up' was in more perfect harmony with the tones of the drama." According to the *Athenaeum*, "The best praise of this superb spectacle is, that it assists materially in carrying on the business of the play. . . . The scenery is not a mere succession of bright prospects and sumptuous interiors; it has a pictorial character in accordance with the action." The *Times'* account catches the sense of *movement* on the stage particularly vividly:

> Mr. Macready has brought before the eyes of his audience an animated picture of those Gothic times which are so splendidly illustrated by the drama. The stage is thronged with the stalwart forms of the middle ages, the clang of battle sounds behind the scenes, massive fortresses bound the horizon. The grouping is admirably managed. The mailed figures now sink into stern tranquillity; now, when the martial fire touches them, they rouse from their lethargy and thirst for action. The sudden interruption in the third act to the temporary peace between John and Philip Augustus was a fine instance of the power of making the stage a living picture. The Englishmen and Frenchmen who had mingled together parted with the rapidity of lightning, the hurried movements, the flashing swords, bespoke the turbulent spirit of the old barons. A quiet mass of glittering accoutrements had suddenly burst into new combinations of animation and energy.

It was "an embodied picture," declared the *Spectator*: "We say *a* picture, for though composed of a succession of scenes, these form parts of a coherent whole . . . the pictorial effects harmonizing with the nature of each incident: in a word, the scenes are a mute chorus, presenting in a visible shape those circumstances and comments which it was the office of the chorus to suggest to the audience when the scenic art was in its infancy." Then follows a wonderfully vivid account, almost scene by scene, of how the stage looked and what it meant to the spectators:

In the first scene, King John is in the plenitude of his power, enthroned and surrounded by his Barons, hurling defiance to the French King; the Gothic hall, hung with tapestry below, but above showing the bare stone walls, adorned with only a square canopy over the chair of state, and the carved timbers of the roof, exhibiting the rude pomp of elder days. In the next scene [II.1], the chivalry of France and England, arrayed in the glittering panoply of war, meet before the gates of Angiers; the lofty ramparts and bastions of the town, stretching out in dim perspective along the river's bank, frown defiance on the rival forces; and while the two Monarchs hold parley with the citizens on the walls, we have full opportunity to note the details of this sumptuous and striking scene. The quaint heraldic devices on the shields and surcoats of the knights enliven with their gaudy hues the glitter of their coats of mail; the regal habiliments of the kings, the flowing robes of the ladies, the parti-coloured habits of the heralds, and the flaunting banners, adding a brighter glow to this warlike pomp: the host of warriors are in frequent action, and the shifting of the throng as each party advance and retire produces new combinations of colour that prevent the eye from being fatigued. In the succeeding scene [III.1], the arrival of the Pope's Legate swells the pageant with the pomp of the Romish Church, and brings new elements of discord into play: the frantic grief of Queen Constance now casts a shade of gloom over the dazzling scene; and the subsequent entrance of King John [III.3], defeated and cast down, attended by only a few dejected followers, prepares the way for the catastrophe of Prince Arthur's death. [John was in fact victorious at this point, not defeated; the reviewer was misled by the "dark transition" which Macready here effected.] The contrast of this and the following scenes with those that have gone before is striking to the most careless spectator: John is seen again enthroned [IV.2], but shorn alike of pomp and power; his abasement before the Pope's Legate [V.1] is followed by a second defeat in his own kingdom [V.3]; his death by poison concluding the tragedy. The management of the shadows of the picture is equally artistical with that of the lights: the lurid atmosphere of the battle-field, and the dim moonlight over Swinstead Abbey [V.5], precede the pall of night that hangs over the death-scene of the King.

The Scenic Artist

The artist who effected these splendid scenes was a young man named William Telbin (1813-73), who was to become one of the most distinguished scene painters of the century, and was a popular easel painter as well. The son of an actor named John Telbin, he was painting stage scenes at Exeter as early as 1832. This *King John* production marked his debut in a major theatre in London. Macready's only significant diary entry concerning Telbin is of July 14, 1842, apparently at the point of sealing Telbin's commission: "Gave the morning to the consideration of the plan and estimates of the scenery for *King John,* by Telbin. Wrote a letter to him with an offer of £250 and directions for several scenes." It was typical of Macready to treat his scenic artists rather summarily. Except on the few occasions when he could persuade the great Clarkson Stanfield to paint for him, he seems to have regarded his artists merely as servants of the establishment, whose job was only to put into effect his own "directions for several scenes." That all-important line of credit, "The Scenery by Mr. Telbin," did not appear on the *King John* playbills until the seventh performance, on November 14.

Those whose business it was to know however, knew. When *King John* opened, the critic of the *Spectator* hailed Telbin at once as "an artist of superior power, imbued with the spirit of the drama," and *John Bull* credited him with "fancy in design," "breadth of style," and "a force, arising out of his power to punctuate his ideas, in which he has no rival." But *John Bull* was not wholly pleased with the newcomer's first accomplishment at the National Theatre, and proceeded to read the young man an avuncular lecture on the mysteries of his craft — a scrap of writing most illuminative of the technique of scene painting in the days before limelight, and wonderfully suggestive of Telbin's romantic style. According to *John Bull,* Telbin shared with the whole tribe of scene painters (Stanfield alone excepted) an ignorance of "the capabilities and nature of the *materiel* he employs." His technical "failure" is analyzed in the following terms:

In distemper red and yellow are powerful, while blue, always impure, is generally feeble; and by these qualities the artist is called on to support the strong in such a manner that by contrast he shall give a seeming strength to the weak. This is the whole problem, and our scene painters work on the opposite principle. Shading with black, the red and yellow is impoverished; and black harmonizing with blue, the latter color is made to appear more weak and more impure. The contrary was Mr. Stanfield's method: all his shadows were deeply browned, whereby the richer colours were enriched, while blue, placed in direct and violent contrast, from position gained what it by nature was deficient in. Mr. Telbin, though he employs no more black than the others of his craft, yet uses it to an extent that lessens the truth of his conceptions. Many of his scenes, especially the forward ones, were boldly and broadly laid in — the Battle-field near St. Edmund's particularly so; and as he is young, and not devoid of intelligence, if he studies carefully he may advance high in a sphere of art that has been proved to be a road to academic honour.

The implications of this critique are vivid, but they become especially meaningful because of the happy circumstance that the watercolor designs for the scenes here referred to have been preserved, so that, at the Folger Shakespeare Library, one can look at almost the very thing the critic was criticizing.

In 1846, when George Ellis sent Charles Kean a transcription of Macready's prompt-book, he also sent with it Telbin's fourteen scene designs, annotated on facing pages with carpenter's notes showing how the scenes were to be built and mounted in the grooves and entrances. In the more complicated scenes, in which separate units were to stand at different levels of the stage, the pieces have been separately painted and laid upon each other, so that on turning the pages one gets something of the effect of a children's "pop-up" book. Presumably Kean used these designs, or adapted them, for his production at the Park Theatre in New York City: the evidence for this supposition will be discussed later. In any case Kean preserved them, having them bound in exactly the same style as the prompt-book — in dark marbled boards with black leather backing and corner-tips, filigreed with gold, and with a cover label gold-stamped Mr CHARLES KEAN. The volume is shelved with the Kean prompt-books at the Folger Shakespeare Library.

The evidence that these scene designs are indeed Telbin's is circumstantial but sufficient. The fact that they are accompanied by notes in Ellis' hand, and the fact that because of their distinctive binding they are to be associated with Kean's 1846 prompt-book and production, and not some later event, are matters that point certainly to an origin in Macready's production of 1842. There had been no other production of *King John* from which Ellis *could* have derived them. And this is but one more of many transmissions of Macready materials, from Ellis to Kean, which may be examined in the Kean collection at the Folger. In December, 1845, Ellis sent Kean a prompt-book of *The Two Gentlemen of Verona* with accompanying ink sketches of scenes; in January, 1846, a prompt-book of *Comus*; in July, 1846, a prompt-book of *Macbeth;* in November, 1846, a prompt-book of *Othello,* with separate volumes of scenes and costumes; in November, 1846, a prompt-book of *The Merchant of Venice,* with separate volumes of scenes and costumes; in January, 1847, a prompt-book of *Cymbeline,* with separate volumes of scenes and costumes; in May, 1848, a prompt-book of *Henry VIII*; in December, 1849, a prompt-book of *Julius Caesar*; in 1850, a prompt-book of *As You Like It.* In the light of this history of Ellis' pollen-bearing, it is in no way surprising that, having the Telbin designs at hand, he sent them, too.

The *Spectator* review, which I have quoted in the preceding section, contains various details which match these pictures unmistakably. The first scene is described exactly as we find it painted: "The Gothic hall, hung with tapestry below, but above showing the bare stone walls, adorned with only a square canopy over the chair of state, and the carved timbers of the roof." In the second scene the *Spectator* speaks of "the lofty ramparts and bastions of the town, stretching out in dim perspective along the river's bank." The *Athenaeum* mentions "the sunny landscape with its shining river before Angiers"; in the middle distance of the Act II set a "river" is discernible flowing through the valley far below. Of the final scenes the *Athenaeum* mentions "the moonlit towers of Swinstead Abbey, and the twilight gloom of the death-scene of the king"; the *Spectator* speaks of "the dim moonlight over Swinstead Abbey" and "the pall of night that hangs over the death-scene of the King."

Finally, let us revert to *John Bull's* caveat against Telbin's practice of shading with black, his combinations of black and blue, and, by implication, his generally dark palette. Certainly *John Bull* is referring specifically to the gorgeously painted blue-black gloom of the Swinstead Abbey scenes (V.5 and 6), and perhaps to the gray stone walls of the throne room (I.1 and IV.2) and the Templars' Church (V.1), and to the olive stone walls of the blinding scene (IV.1). The artist's error was that he painted his stage pictures as if they were easel pictures, using those colors which stated his intentions directly, as if the pictures were to be seen by fair daylight on a gallery wall. He failed to reckon with the vast depths and distances of the stage of Drury Lane Theatre, and with the softening and darkening effect of stage gas-light. Brown, says *John Bull,* is the only available color for shadowing. Sixteen years later, we can observe, Telbin had thoroughly learned this valuable lesson. In 1858 at the Princess's Theatre, when in association with Thomas Grieve and others he helped prepare the scenes for Charles Kean's final revival of *King John* (in which, as we shall later see, were repeated or imitated several of his 1842 designs), he discarded his dark palette altogether: dark blues and blacks disappear, all grays become tans, and the darkest shadows are a rusty brown. The queer result is that while the water-color sketches for Macready's production are "beautiful" and those for Kean's are "garish," it is probable that the sets in Kean's theatre were more effective because they were more visible under the stage illumination of that time.

The Stage of Drury Lane Theatre

The scenic arrangements at Drury Lane Theatre in 1842 were still based on the old wing and groove system, which provided facilities, at least within the acts, for instantaneous change of scene in full view of the audience. Reference to the floor plan and longitudinal cross section of the theatre and the stage, here reprinted (Figures 1 and 2) from Charles Dibdin's *History and Illustrations of the London Theatres* (1826), will equip the reader with a basic image of the system and of the major dimensions in which Macready's actors and carpenters worked. The proscenium opening at the curtain line was forty feet wide, reducible to about thirty-five feet by movable panels. The forestage, flanked by boxes, extended about twelve feet forward from the curtain line; there were no stage doors onto the forestage at this time, all entrances and exits being made behind the curtain line by way of the entrances between the "wings." The stage behind the curtain line was forty-eight feet deep and about eighty feet from wall to wall. Beyond this eighty-foot width there were twenty-foot-deep scene docks at either side. The entire stage, from orchestra to back wall, was gently raked to improve visibility, rising perhaps three feet in sixty. The stage was generously trapped (or equipped with "sliders"), especially in the middle and upstage areas, so that entrances, including massive ones, could be made up ramps or stairs from the "mezzanine" below.

Throughout the depth of the stage there were spaced pairs of "grooves" for the sliding on and off of scenery painted on "pairs of flats" and "wings": each set of grooves contained three or four slots so that more than one combination of flats and wings could be readied at a time. Dibdin pictures six pairs of grooves, but the grooves were removable and their number was revisable: as we discover from the prompt-book of *King John* there were seven pairs

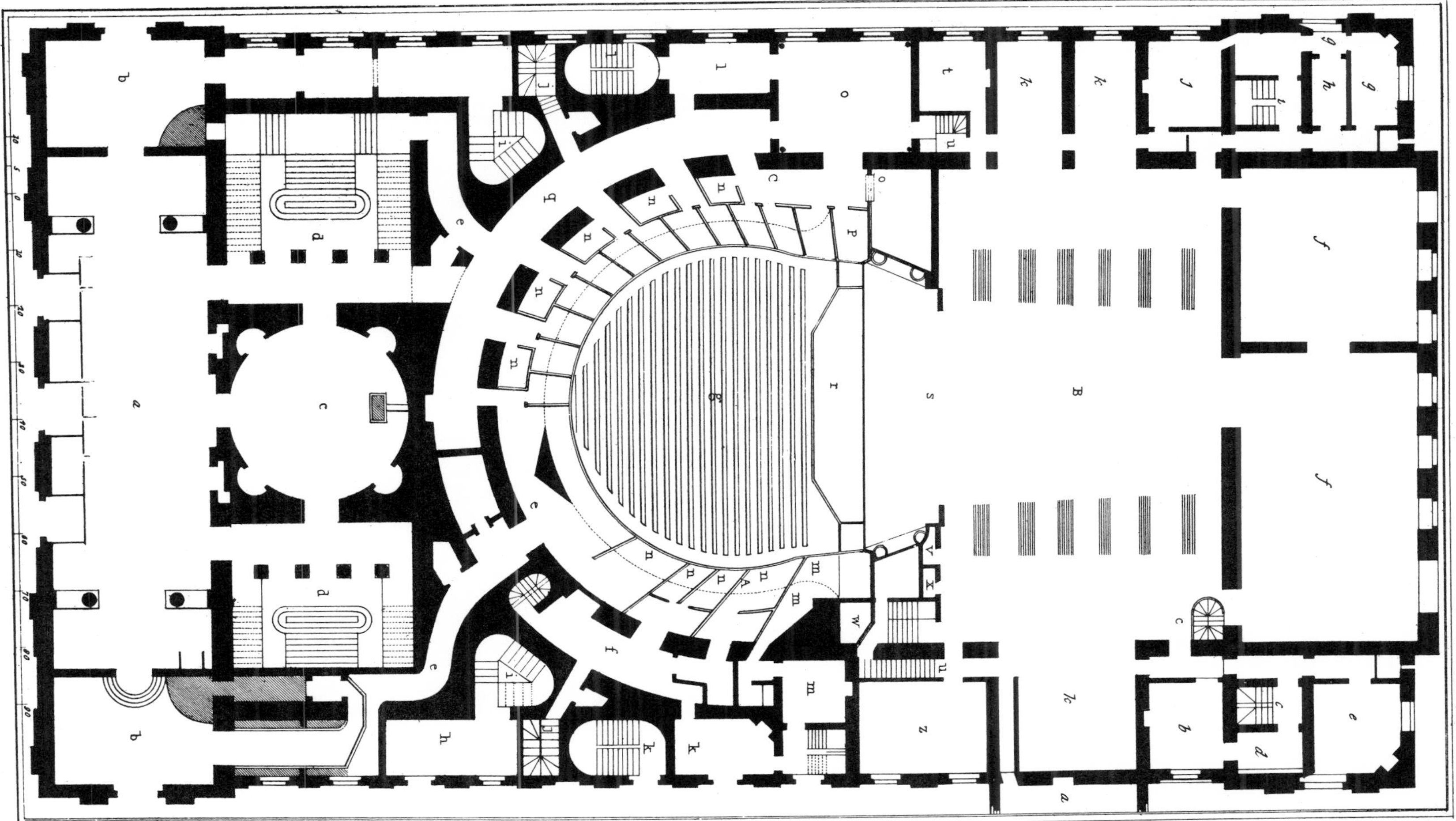

Figure 1. Drury Lane Theatre floor plan

available in 1842. The floor grooves were matched by overhead grooves attached to the underside of the fly galleries at either side of the stage, and these overhead grooves were equipped with hinged extensions which when dropped into place would hold the flats erect as they moved in to meet each other at the center of the stage. The spaces between the sets of grooves were called the "entrances," each taking its number from the number of the groove behind it: thus "1 E.L." was the entrance at stage left between the curtain line and the first groove; "3 E.R." was the entrance between the second and third grooves at stage right.

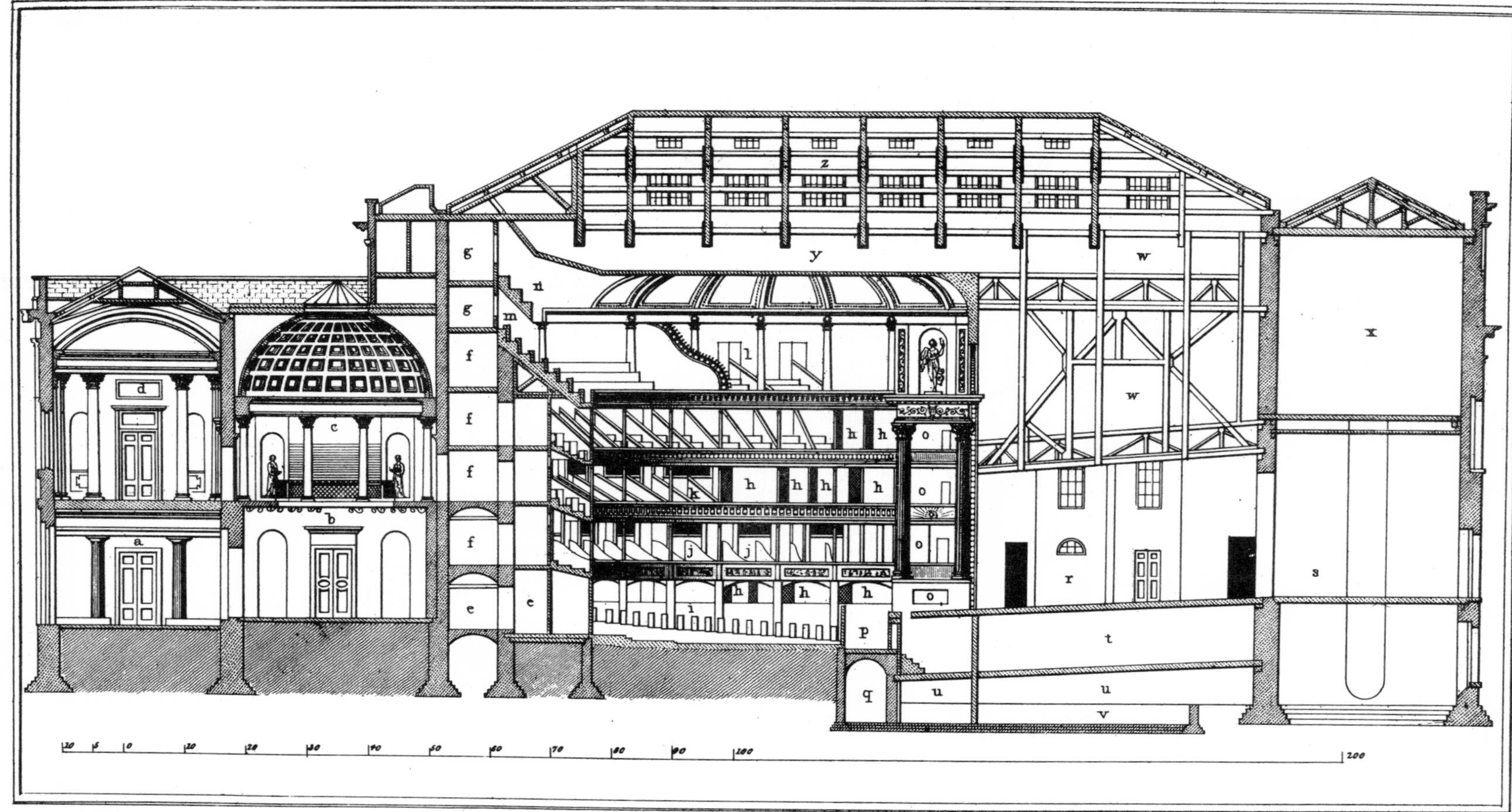

Figure 2. Drury Lane Theatre longitudinal section from east to west

The usual manner of presenting a "scene" was to paint it on a pair of flats which slid on from the sides and met at center. Occasionally in a "deep" scene the farthest view — a skyscape, usually — was painted on a "cloth" or "drop" which hung at the back of the stage, or, say, in the "seventh entrance." If the pair of flats was set in one of the upstage pair of grooves, it would be dressed at the sides by "wings" set in the forward grooves and by "borders" hung from above in the forward "entrances." Dibdin tells us that at Drury Lane the flats were twenty-one feet tall and each half fourteen feet wide; that the wings were twenty-one feet tall and from five to eight feet wide. It is difficult to see how a twenty-eight-foot-wide scene could fill a thirty-five to forty-foot proscenium opening; but the addition of eight-foot wings at either side would fairly well complete the expanse, and there were also available movable masking pieces called "tormentors" to fill up the gaps in the first entrances. Even so Her Majesty's view from the Royal Box, which flanked the right side of the forestage, must often have included a lively prospect of off-stage activity through the stage left entrances.

The pair of flats might present a solid surface or a surface with openings cut in it. "Cut flats" were very popular in forest scenes to represent seemingly free-standing trees and bushes; or, as in *King John,* they might be used to reveal a distant landscape seen from inside an interior, or a deeper interior seen through an archway of a great hall. Practical doors were sometimes built into the sliding flats. Three-dimensional units, called "set pieces" and representing buildings, were sometimes set at the side entrances where they could be easily thrust on and drawn off by the carpenters; or they might be set more centrally in the upstage areas where they could be "discovered" and concealed again by flat scenes moving off or on in the grooves in front of them. When furniture was used, it too was discovered and concealed, when possible, by the movement of downstage flat scenes. Sometimes, however, it was thrust on and drawn off along with the flats and wings. On rare occasions furniture that stood near the center of the stage had to be placed or removed by supernumeraries or carpenters within view of the audience.

The Costumes

Mrs. Lisa Puckle, whose father, the late Sir Nevil Macready, was Macready's youngest son, recently discovered among her papers a packet of thirty-nine sheets of water-color costume designs which survived the destruction of Macready's personal papers after the 1913 publication of his *Diaries.* Twelve of the sheets, containing fifteen figures, are designs for *King John* (Figures 3 to 6) — all that remain of at least twenty-eight sheets that once existed. They are unsigned, but comparison with other signed costume designs in the Charles Kean collection at the Folger Shakespeare Library reveals them to be unmistakably the work of Colonel Charles Hamilton Smith, the well-known antiquarian, historian, and naturalist of Plymouth, who over the years supplied both Macready and Kean with historical data for their classical revivals.

The primary research into the historical antecedents for the costumes of *King John* had been done in 1823 by J. R. Planché for the famous revival of the play by Charles Kemble. Planché published his notes and twenty figures in *Dramatic Costume,* no. 1: *Costume of Shakespeare's Historical Tragedy of King John* (London, 1823). The lithographed figures, by J. K. Meadows, are hand tinted. Smith followed Planché's well-informed authority in many of the important dresses (as did Charles Kean), adding to his sketches, however, certain decorative details which enhance their stage beauty. Since it is not practicable to reproduce Smith's designs in color, I append the following notes, which may be compared with Planché's notes (reprinted in the *New Variorum Edition* of *King John,* pp. 664-669), with Planché's tinted lithographs (by anyone so fortunate as to have access to this rare work), and with Charles Kean's notes in the *Modern Standard Drama.* The numbering of my notes follows the numbering of Smith's sheets.

1. King John's first dress, based on his effigy in the choir of Worcester Cathedral. The gown is rose-red with a flowered border; the belt white, the gloves green and jeweled, the sword gold-handled in a blue sheath. The undergown is green with yellow borders. The robe is gold with jeweled collar and borders. The footwear consists of crimson stockings and black shoes. The coronet is gold, jeweled, with a crimson undercap.

14. Queen Elinor, from her effigy in the Abbey of Fontevrault. Planché, following the authority of Montfauçon, gave her a dark

blue robe sprinkled with gold flowers and a white dress sprinkled with red and blue flowers. Smith reproduced the form of the effigy as to crown, headdress, collar, and so on, and gave her a dark blue robe (but without flowers). The dress is of alternate squares of orange and yellow, with a green figure on the yellow squares. The sleeves are rose-red.

2. King Philip. Planché invented a suit of silver chain mail and a surcoat of blue with gold cross stripes. Smith presented Philip in royal robes: a blue gown with gold fleurs-de-lis and border; a darker blue robe, ermine-lined, with gold fleurs-de-lis; white jeweled gloves; a rose-red undergown with gold border. (The shoes and the crown are not tinted.)

3. Robert Faulconbridge. Planché, following the model of some enameled figures on King John's silver cup at King's Lynn, presented a figure in rose-pink hose, a gray knee-length coat with blue edging, and a short blue cloak. Smith's wholly different design shows a brown undergown and a white overgown with a huge blue lion rampant; the band falling across the chest from the right shoulder is yellow. A note on the back of the sheet indicates that Philip Faulconbridge wore the same costume, as if it were the uniform of the family.

5. Lady Faulconbridge, "from the effigy of Lady Harcourt? in Gloucester Cathedral." Planché's costume, based on a manuscript illustration in the Harleian Library, is a simple combination of lemon-yellow dress and blue robe lined with white. Smith's is more colorful. In the white squares of the dress are repeated the blue lions banded with yellow from 3; the alternate squares are red. The sleeves are yellow. The robe is white, lined with green, and apparently a huge blue lion rampant covers the back. The headdress is white.

17. Blanch of Castile, "from the costume of Jane of Boulogne, 1236." Planché, working from engravings in Montfauçon, gave her a rose-red robe over a white dress. Smith, electing simply a young noblewoman of the period as model, provided a very different image. The overgown is rose-red, with gold collar, belt, border, and castle design; the undergown and sleeves are blue on white; a long white veil falls from the gold coronet.

7. The Notarius Apostolicus wears a lavender cowl and robe over a black gown. The bag of papal documents is crimson velvet decorated with figures in white and gold.

6. Cardinal Pandulph, "from the supposed oldest figure of a Cardinal in Italy." Planché presented Pandulph in red robes over a white undergown, and *hatless,* because cardinals were not granted the red hat until the Council of Lyons in 1245. Smith acknowledged this fact of history on the reverse of the sheet, but applied the red hat anyway. The robes are red, the underdress a white surplice over a dark blue gown.

15. Constance, "from the effigy of Mathilde de Boulogne, 1211." Planché, citing only Montfauçon, gave Constance a very bright costume: a purple dress with little squares outlined in gold all over it, a bright green robe with white lining and a broad gold border around the bottom, a jeweled gold crown and a white headdress. Smith, perhaps more sensitive to the dramatic effect of the character, garbed her more soberly. The dress is gray, with gold belt and collar; the robe is black, lined with rose; the crown-like headdress is red, with a black veil falling from it.

28. The Archbishop of Canterbury, "from a St. Dunstan of XII Century." "A Bishop in ordinary dress." The Archbishop's robes are blue trimmed with white, red, and gold; the sleeves are red, the gloves white. The undergown is white. The miter is white and gold. The Bishop appears to be in blue robes with a short red cloak.

11. The English herald. The cap and collar are red on the right, yellow on the left; the gown reverses these colors; the badge shows a yellow lion on a red ground. The French herald is in blue and white, and the fleur-de-lis on his badge is yellow.

8. The crosier bearer wears a black headdress, blue and tan shoulder cape, white surplice, and black gown. The templar's dress is white, with cap and cross of bright red.

Figure 3. Costumes designed for King John, Queen Elinor, and King Philip

Figure 4. Costumes designed for Robert Faulconbridge, Lady Faulconbridge, and Blanche of Castile

Figure 5. Costumes designed for Notarius Apostolicus, Cardinal Pandulph, and Constance

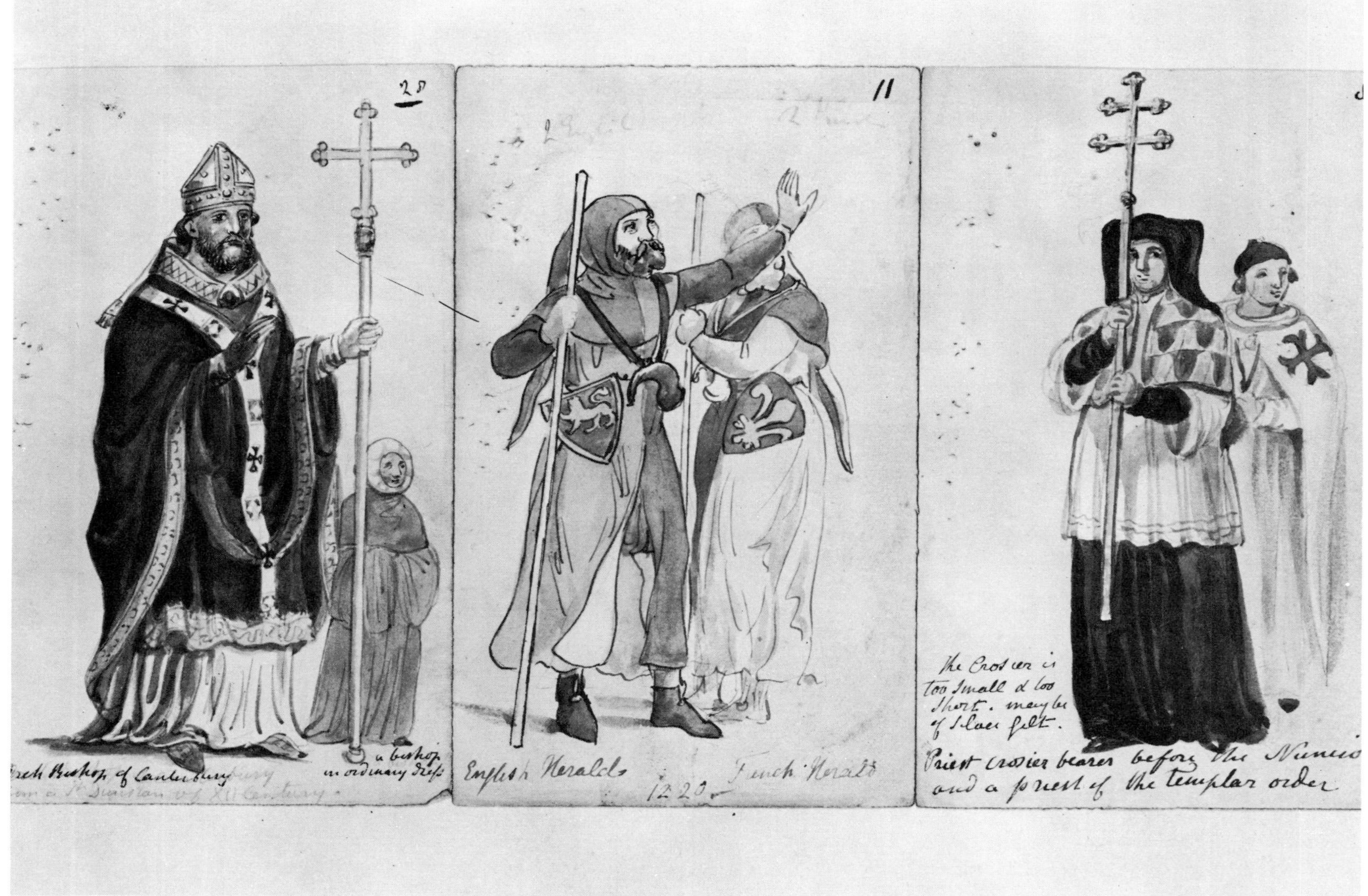

Figure 6. Costumes designed for the Archbishop of Canterbury and a Bishop, the English and French heralds, the Crosier bearer and a templar

The Staging

The following notes are not intended to describe Macready's production in every detail, or to "tell the story of the play." The reader will find his own total image of the production through combinative inspection of the prompt-book, the scene designs (Figures 7 to 20), and the costume designs (Figures 3 to 6). I wish here simply to call attention to certain salient features of the staging, including the construction and manipulation of the scenic units, and to supplement the evidence of the prompt-book and the plates with evidence from other sources. In analyzing the scenery, for instance, I have quoted liberally from George Ellis' carpenter's notes. A few details about stage arrangements and playing time are derived from John Willmott's notes in the "Original prompt-book" — that is, the actual working prompt-book used at Drury Lane. When I quote specific stage directions I have usually transcribed them from Macready's preparation copy rather than from the Ellis-Kean copy. Thus the curious reader may at least occasionally compare Macready's original intention with Ellis' recording of the final effect — and observe that "between the idea and the reality, between the motion and the act," the shadows that fall are really very faint.

THE STAGING OF I.1. Hall of State in King John's Palace (276 lines cut to 204) (see Figure 7). At 7:00 P.M. the orchestra struck up the overture, which consisted of "martial music" from Beethoven's *Fifth Symphony* and was perhaps three or four minutes long. The act drop rose with a long flourish of trumpets (two trumpeters were stationed off-stage left) to reveal a splendidly decorated and peopled throne room. The throne itself, on its dais and under its canopy — all blood red — was set in a wide arched alcove upstage center, apparently just beyond the fourth grooves. The windowed wall behind the throne, according to Ellis' notes, was a "Cloth 5 Ent." — that is to say, a backdrop hung in the space immediately in front of the fifth grooves. Light (probably not real but painted) streamed down across the throne from stage right. The side walls of the throne room show an interesting departure from standard scenic practice of the time. They were *not* expressed by a series of four pairs of wings set in the grooves and painted to simulate perspective continuity. They were "2 pair of flats, set oblique" — that is, solid flats somewhat over twenty feet long, proceeding from the front corners of the stage (probably from the first grooves) and raking toward center across the second and third grooves to the fourth grooves. They were painted to show gray stone and high windows in their upper halves and reddish brown tapestry hangings below. The left wall was pierced by a tall arched doorway near the downstage end, apparently giving into the "second entrance." The borders overhead contributed height and depth and grace to the room by showing five receding sets of hammerbeam oaken arches: the first three of these were apparently separate cloths hung in the first, second, and third "entrances" (that is, hung from rigging which operated immediately downstage from the first, second, and third grooves); the farthest two were perhaps painted on a single cloth hung in the fourth entrance.

King John was seen on his throne, conversing with Norfolk, who stood at the foot of the dais slightly to John's left. Seated on a stool to his right was his mother Queen Elinor, and de Warrenne and the archbishop were on the dais steps at right and left respectively. Forty-four attendants — lords, ladies, bishops, knights, heralds, and so on — filled the stage at right, left, and forward, all turned toward the King. The trumpet flourish continued while Norfolk and two heralds, at a sign from the King, left the stage by the down-left doorway and brought back the French Ambassador Chatillon and his company. When King John spoke the opening words, there were fifty-nine persons on the stage. The management of the crowd was carefully planned. At Chatillon's entrance, Macready wrote in his preparation copy, "The circle breaks asunder . . . and the attention of all on the scene is given to the proceedings of the Embassy." When Chatillon was conducted out by Pembroke and others (line 30), "the Court breaks up into small circles of conversation, as if relating to the King." When King John came off the dais to discuss the case of the Faulconbridge brothers (line 129), "the Nobles approach the King as if speaking of the litigants." Macready was famous for his handling of crowd scenes, which he had exhibited in earlier years in his staging of *Coriolanus* and *Henry V* at Covent Garden. Westland Marston preserves for us a glimpse of Macready's rehearsal of one of these scenes of *King John*:

The groupings of that play, and the stage business in general, were elaborate enough to account for, and almost excuse the manager's impatience. Very striking, however, was his sudden change from angry excitement, when addressing his "supers," to his unruffled courtesy of tone and look when he turned to myself or others of his acquaintance on the stage. . . . I conceived an impression, which still remains, that his bursts of temper were far more under his control than perhaps he himself supposed, and that he was sometimes inclined to exaggerate them that they might contrast with his after-smoothness — that he was exhibiting, in short, his beloved stage transitions in real life [*Our Recent Actors,* I, 66].

The act drop fell after seventeen minutes of playing time, at about 7:20 P.M. It stayed down, one would guess, for a five-minute entr'acte, while the orchestra resumed the music of the *Fifth Symphony*: not only must the actors "All change to Armour," but the elaborate first act set had to be replaced by an even more elaborate one for the second act. It is, in fact, nearly incredible that the scene change could have been made so swiftly. But Ellis records that the "waits" during the total performance totaled only eighteen minutes, and Willmott's clocking of certain of the act-endings confirms this figure. We are compelled to believe that Macready's carpenters and the Drury Lane stage machinery were magically efficient.

THE STAGING OF II.1. Before the Gates of Angiers (598 lines cut to 395) (see Figure 8). The act drop rose amidst a flourishing of trumpets from right and left as King Philip and the French party met the Duke of Austria before the entrance postern of the castle of Angiers. At stage left were the fortified castle walls, painted in somber browns, tans, and greens. At stage right was shown a part of the French encampment and beyond it "landscape." In the middle distance the river Maine flowed down its valley, and mountains were seen beyond it. Over all was a fair-weather sky.

In order to prepare this scene, Telbin must have visited Angiers (modern Angers), for his images appear to have been derived from observations taken on the spot. One can find his viewing point by standing in the Place du Chateau a little distance from the southeast corner of the castle and looking down along the great south wall westward toward the river. Telbin treated the observed elements with poetic freedom, of course: he omitted the moat, reduced the number of towers in his line of vision from five to four, brought round the entrance postern from the opposite northern wall and placed it in the foreground of his picture (where the tiny field gate should be), changed the nearest towers from cylindrical to rectangular, and suppressed the curious color pattern of the walls (white stone banding on blackish slate) for which the castle is famous. He also romantically exaggerated the mountainousness of the landscape and terrain, and, as appears in later scenes, conceived the castle as standing upon an isolated and very precipitous hill. Yet for all these changes, he has caught very well the essential shape and spirit of the place. And had anyone pointed out to him that the castle was not built in its extant form until a generation after the Shakespearean events, he would have dismissed such quibbling with Shakespearean indifference.

The stage right details of camp and landscape are not shown in the water color, but they are clearly specified in Ellis' carpenter's notes. Probably this means that although Telbin did not include them in his original design, he added them when he executed the scene for the stage. It is in fact unlikely that the French camp *could* have stood on this narrow hilltop *as Telbin imagined it,* and according to the evidence of the very next scene the tent of the French King stood on the plains below: from inside that tent we see the rest of the camp and beyond it the hill and castle in the distance. But to balance the stage and use the stage right grooves, Telbin had to find some relevant subject matter, and hit upon this easy expedient. In Kean's productions the stage right area was more sensibly filled up with a huge scaling engine or catapulting machine — a scenic device which Macready already exploited in his Covent Garden production of *Henry V* in 1839.

Ellis' carpenter's notes show us exactly how this immense scene was put together and how it worked. The nearest tower in the castle walls, at downstage left, was a three-dimensional piece, set from the first grooves. Within the top of it hung a "Small platform slung from flies 2 E L," on which apparently stood one or more Angevin sentinels. The castle-gates unit occupied the third entrance left, with a platform and steps behind it to accommodate the crowd of ten Angevin citizens who appeared above to insist upon the independence of their city. Late in the act when the great gates were opened, a mighty crashing of "Heavy Iron Bolt and Chain," manipulated by the prompter or his assistant off-stage left, intensified the realism of the scene. The second tower, just beyond the gates unit, was probably (Ellis fails to mention this section) another three-dimensional piece. The next unit, including the round tower and the rocks on which it stood, was painted on a flat which was set in the fourth grooves ("1/2 Castle flat 4 WL"). The farthest portion of the castle and its rock base was another flat which was perhaps set obliquely in the sixth entrance ("1/2 Castle flat back of 5 Gr L"). The sky was represented on a "cloth" hung in the seventh entrance. The far-off mountains and the river were evidently not painted on this cloth, but were "3 set rock rows, front of cloth." On the right side of the stage, the French tents were represented by wings in the first, second, and third grooves; beyond them were landscape wings in the fourth, fifth, and sixth grooves. It is clear enough from the picture that the fortification is on a rocky eminence, but this fact was emphasized by a special device in the upstage right area. "Back slider open," Ellis noted; "Rake piece in front to join 5WR." This means that at the sixth entrance the stage right section of the floor was slid away, the opening being masked by a ground row in front of it; and that a stairway or ramp came up from beneath the stage, so that the arrival of Chatillon and his party, and later King John and the English host, was "up rake as from the plains below."

The opening trumpets of the scene brought thirty-six performers upon the stage: four Angevin sentinels "discovered" on the ramparts, eight Austrians arriving (below the castle) from the first entrance left, and twenty-four of the French party (including the King, the Dauphin, Constance, and Arthur) from the first three entrances on the right. The arrival of Chatillon's party from the valley below (line 49) raised the number to forty-six. The army of King John (line 83) raised the number to eighty-two. When the full complement of Angevin citizens appeared above the gates (line 200), the total was eighty-eight. At line 121, when Elinor and Constance first intrude into the quarrel between the kings, Macready followed the Kemble example of transposing to this position a later passage (lines 163-177) in which the ladies berate each other over the gentle protest of little Arthur. This has the advantage, since lines 122 to 133 were cut, of varying the voices in the quarrel, and of better motivating the line, "Women and fools, break off your conference." For some reason Ellis *failed to mark this transposition in the prompt-book he prepared for Charles Kean,* with the result that Kean did not use it and it does not appear in any of the printed acting versions which derived from Kean's book.

The off-stage battle at line 299 is obviously a clumsy thing to get around, especially in a scenic theatre, where the larger the armies, the greater the traffic problem. In Bell's edition Francis Gentleman proposed that the battle be eliminated entirely, to "save the stunned ears of an audience, from much unnecessary drumming and trumpeting." Macready rearranged the lines slightly in order to spread out the mass exits and make them more manageable and the battle more credible. The bulk of the French party went off through the stage right entrances at line 287, when Philip cried "Mount, chevaliers! To arms!" King John and the Bastard then spoke lines 295 to 297, "Up higher to the plain," and so on, and the English forces began to move down the ramp in the sixth entrance right. Philip and Lewis concluded a whispered conference with "It shall be so," and went off right immediately after the battle cry at line 299, "God, and our right!" (which, by the way, is one of the very rare occasions in Macready's theatre when the word "God" was not piously translated into "Heaven"). Austria crossed left and sent his party out the first entrance left. The Bastard meanwhile remained with one attendant up center, bracing on his shield, and roaring lines 288 to 290 to invoke "St. George, that swinged the dragon." Seeing Austria cross to exit at the right he hurled after him the taunting lines 290 to 294, then followed King John down the ramp. Then, as Ellis' directives make clear, the "Shouts, Crashes, Trumpet Alarums" that made up the noise of battle were "done 3 distinct times!!! — commencing each time, very loud, and concluding very remote." The stage was not left empty during the battle: "The Citizens seem to watch the Battle, from the walls." The *Times* critic was much taken with their watching: "To the smallest *minutiae* was this attention to what may be called the decorative characters of the piece directed. The citizens of Angiers . . . whose countenances eagerly followed the various movements in the distance, may be mentioned as a minor instance of excellent training for a complete effect." When the battle was over and the French and English heralds had in turn demanded the opening of the castle gates (line 333), all the parties returned very rapidly and occupied their previous positions, except that the Austrians, who had been at stage left, now entered intermingled with the French at stage right. The mass movements throughout the sequent action — as the French and English join forces to attack the city, draw their swords to rush off to their stations, break into different groups to make conversation about the marriage proposal, sheathe their swords and "mingle together courteously & friendlily" when the marriage of Lewis and Blanch is agreed upon, and exit in procession into the castle shouting "very joyously" at the end — are specifically and vividly visualized at every turn.

The act drop fell after what Ellis calls twenty-six minutes of playing time, and this timing is confirmed by John Willmott's clocking the act end as at "10– to 8." The orchestra played more Beethoven during another four- or five-minute entr'acte while this elaborate set was disposed of and the stage was arranged for the third act.

THE STAGING OF III.1. Interior of French King's Tent (347 lines cut to 217) (see Figure 9). Flats in the third grooves represented the vast rectangular interior of the tent with its brown ceiling, dark blue side walls, and golden posts hung with arms and banners. Presumably, though Ellis does not say so, the scene was brought forward by borders above and by wings in the second and first grooves. The third groove flats comprised a "cut flat" — that is, they showed a large opening at upstage center, beyond which, in the fifth grooves, another pair of flats showed the sky, and a ground row in front of it depicted a tented camp and the castle of Angiers on the hilltop. At stage left, apparently at the second entrance, stood a canopied dais with King Philip's chair of state upon it, and beside it another chair to be placed upon it later for King John. A table with a crucifix on it stood at the right.

The scene began with only Constance, Arthur, and Salisbury present, but from the distance one heard the shouts and trumpet flourishes of the approaching French, English, and Austrian hosts. When these arrived, after line 74, and Cardinal Pandulph entered with his retinue at line 134, the stage contained about the same number of actors as in the preceding scene: the ten actors who had played the citizens of Angiers had now regarbed themselves as ecclesiasts and knights templars attendant upon Pandulph. Again the crowd movements and reactions are dictated with care. When the nobles came into the tent, they looked at Constance, who had thrown herself on the ground, "with extreme surprise." At Pandulph's entrance they bowed "very low" and regarded him with "Deepest silence and attention." When King John defied Pandulph, "all look alarmed at John's temerity." At the sentence of excommunication there was a "Shudder and sensation of horror through the assembly." As the quarrel between King John and Philip grew hotter their partisans grew more anxious and more excited until at Philip's "England, I will fall from thee" (line 320), there was "general excitement and movement. — Nobles bracing on their shields, preparing for battle, and crowding round their respective Kings." The end of the scene was all "Tumult and discordant cries and orders" as the hosts poured out of the tent to do battle. The noise continued, rising and falling in intensity, and Ellis warned Kean's prompter, "quick! — to close in, at 1 Gr."

THE STAGING OF III.2. Battlefield Before Angiers (10 lines) (see Figure 10). A pair of flats depicting a colorful landscape for a battlefield closed together in the first grooves, and thus swiftly was the stage readied for the epic struggle that was to ensue. As the hubbub continued, several parties of French and English fought each other across the forestage from stage left to right, the English prevailing. Then the Bastard entered from the left and spoke his sentence about the devilish heat. The Duke of Austria entered from the right, and the Bastard drove him off right in furious duel. A moment later he returned carrying Austria's lion's skin (not his severed head) as a sign of his triumph. With the words "Austria's head lie there," he hurled the lion's skin off-stage left. More charges, shouts, and alarums. Then a half-dozen English leaders from the right met King John and others of the English party from the left. King John was leading the captured Prince Arthur, whom he threw across the stage to Hubert. After the exchange of sentences between King John and the Bastard about the safety of Queen Elinor, all the English went off-stage left, amid "Charges, — Shouts, — &c. — which gradually subside, — and thro' which various Trumpet Calls are heard, answering each other, — then a Retreat is sounded." Thus was this tiny fragment of the play developed into a major battle scene.

THE STAGING OF III.3. Another part of the battlefield (73 lines) (see Figure 11). After a pause while the retreat sounded ("Give time," is Willmott's penciling), the first groove flats slid away to reveal another and boldly different landscape, the colors now all somber, set in the third grooves. A tented camp was seen in the middle distance, and beyond it the castle of Angiers. In the foreground was a weedy pond, to stage left forbidding bluffs, to stage right scraggly brown leafless trees. The bright sky of the preceding scene had now turned to stormy gray. The trumpet calls gradually died away in the distance as groups of the English (seventeen actors in all) slowly drifted upon the stage, "All as if fatigued with their exertions in the battle." This was a tremendously bold and impressive *coup de théâtre,* by which Macready marked the sudden change of the play from political pageant into dark tragedy, and the character of King John from stalwart leader to furtive cowardly murderer. The critic of the *Times* declared that this dark transition "was artfully managed, both by the actor and the manager," and the evidence of the scene designs helps to clarify that comment. From Westland Marston (*Our Recent Actors,* I, 100) we hear of the impressiveness of another "dark" effect at this point, which is not recorded in the prompt-book: "After the fight in the third act, which results in an English victory, a part of the English force crossed the stage, preceded by trumpeters, who sounded notes of melancholy and wailing. One night, at Macready's house, Mr. W. J. Fox objected that sounds of this kind could not with propriety have proceeded from the triumphant English. . . . Macready answered that the purpose of these notes was to prepare the house for King John's sinister interview with Hubert, which immediately followed." When Queen Elinor drew aside the weeping Prince

Arthur, and King John called Hubert to him, the battle-weary nobles all turned in upon each other, as if in conversation, so that "No face on the stage except Hubert's & John's is turned to the audience" during the dialogue in which King John persuaded Hubert to murder the child. Thus did Macready's managerial cunning call into play every device of scene, sound, and movement to underscore the transition. The scene ended with a slow trumpet march sounding from the distance — "4 Trumpets in Green Room" is Willmott's penciled notation.

THE STAGING OF III.4. Interior of French King's Tent (183 lines cut to 115) (see Figure 9). When the English party had marched off slowly to the left, "towards Calais," the stage was once more transformed into the interior of the French King's tent. The landscape flats were drawn off in the third grooves, revealing the "cut flat" already set in the third grooves and the vista of Angiers through the opening. Simultaneously the ceiling borders were lowered and the tent-wall wings, the throne dais, and the table with crucifix were thrust on at left and right. This, by the way, was the only scene in the production in which a set was used a second time.

The playing time of the third act, comprised of four scenes and reduced from 613 to 415 lines, was forty minutes, according to Ellis' records. Willmott penciled in two clockings — "23– to 9" and "25– to 9" — which closely confirm Ellis' figure. During the brief entr'acte, we assume, the carpenters took advantage of the covering music of the orchestra to set all three scenes of the fourth act, including the heavy castle set of the third scene.

THE STAGING OF IV.1. Vaulted Apartment in Northampton Castle (134 lines cut to 111) (see Figure 12). The ominous vaulted chamber in which Prince Arthur was to be threatened with blinding was painted in gloomy olive grays on a pair of flats in the second grooves, doubtless brought forward by borders and by wings in the first grooves. A practicable door piece, covered with a dark green tapestry, stood in the first entrance left. Just to stage left of center in the back wall there was built into the flat a dark brown practical door, locked with a key; this door was backed by a "chamber piece." The illumination appeared to come from a window, in which stood a crucifix, set between arches at stage right: this was obviously not real light, but only bright paint on flat canvas. The actual stage light was perceptibly reduced to enhance the melodrama gloom of the scene: "Borders down" (meaning "dim the overhead lights") is Ellis' notation for darkening the stage. A heavy antique table and a chair stood at right center. Off-stage left were ready the cords to bind Prince Arthur, the "pan of imitation fire," and a set of blinding irons painted "red hot." At the end of this scene occurred a scenic crux which appears to have been unusual in Macready's productions. The heavy table and chair could not be concealed by running on "front flats," for the following scene required as deep a staging as this one; and they were too near the center of the stage to be drawn off by carpenters working invisibly in the wings. They had to be removed by supernumeraries in sight of the audience. Ellis' directive in Charles Kean's promptbook is that "4 attendants, clear" before the whistle for scene change; and someone has penciled in an indication that the job was done by four English standard bearers. At Drury Lane Macready apparently sent on "non-dramatic" agents: Willmott's notation is that "4 Green Coats dressed clear the Stage." (A "green coat" was a stage attendant.)

THE STAGING OF IV.2. Hall of State (269 lines cut to 219) (see Figure 13). The "vaulted apartment" flats drew off in the second grooves to reveal a throne-room scene also set in the second grooves. This was a "cut flat" with a large round archway in the center giving onto a farther hall painted on flats in the third grooves. Borders presumably were dropped in to represent the heavy square-beamed ceiling, and wings in the first grooves brought the scene forward at the sides. The King's throne on its red-canopied dais (probably the same one used in I.1) was thrust on stage in the second entrance right. Two heralds and a dozen nobles preceded the King, amidst flourishing of trumpets, as King John took the throne after his "second coronation." When King John told them, at line 85, that Arthur was dead, "The Lords start & are much excited," and presently they left "thro' Centre in violent agitation." The restoration of Peter of Pomfret, probably for the first time since Shakespeare's day, added a fine touch of supernatural doom to the latter portion of the play.

THE STAGING OF IV.3. Northampton Castle (159 lines cut to 138) (see Figure 14). The blackish green castle, with flashes of gold light across the tower tops (as if the sun were setting behind it off-stage left), was set far upstage, and was revealed by the sliding off of the second and third groove flats of the preceding scene. The seemingly huge central tower was a three-dimensional piece joined to a wing in the fourth groove. Concealed behind it, in the fifth entrance, was a "High Rostrum" for Prince Arthur to stand upon for his soliloquy and to leap down from. The farther portions of the castle were apparently painted on flats in the fifth and sixth grooves. The sky cloth hung in the seventh entrance. At stage right, not shown in the water color, a "Tree Row" stood in the fifth groove. The low round tower and low gateway at left center stood in the fourth entrance in front of the great tower. Behind it were concealed "6 Men, with carpet . . . to catch P Arthur." When they caught him in their carpet they tumbled him through the gateway down the steps onto the stage — an effect that brought indignant protests from some of the critics. "The death of Arthur is absurdly overdone," said the *Athenaeum*: "Not content with his leaping from a high tower, he is made to roll over and over down the steps as if they were a sloping bank of turf, rather difficult as an involuntary achievement, especially after such a fall." The *Spectator,* too, found this "an exaggeration at once shocking and ludicrous." One cannot help wondering how far the child actress who played Prince Arthur had to fall. The tower looks enormous; but since it was set more than twenty-five feet upstage of the curtain line it was probably not in fact more than a dozen feet tall. A note in the Sadler's Wells prompt-book indicates that Samuel Phelps employed a double, apparently an acrobat, who climbed out a window and dropped down. Professor Sprague records (*Shakespeare and the Actors,* p. 114) one later arrangement whereby the Arthur dropped onto a bed behind a wall, and another whereby a dummy was thrown off the tower top while the actress slid down a perpendicular pole behind the tower.

The fourth act, comprised of three scenes and cut from 562 to 468 lines, was played in thirty-six minutes. During the entr'acte the carpenters could place in their grooves the elements of all six of the scenes that made up the final act.

THE STAGING OF V.1. Interior of Templars' Church, at Northampton (79 lines cut to 74) (see Figure 15). An organ played "Music of the Church" as the act drop rose on this scene of King John's submission to Cardinal Pandulph. The scene had always before this been placed, by editors and producers, at "The Court of England" or "A Room in the Palace," and Charles Kean is credited with being the first to place it in a church (*New Variorum Edition,* p. 351). But it was Macready's invention: in his preparation copy he wrote, "The Temple Church actually at Dover but sup. at Northampton." The round-arched, circular, gray stone interior was painted on a pair of flats (presumably with borders and wings), which Ellis persistently specifies were set in the second grooves, with Pandulph's chair on a canopied dais set in the second entrance left. Macready intended, however, to set the chair in the *third* entrance left, and a note in Kean's hand under Ellis' carpenter's note insists that the flats "Must be in third grooves." The large number of actors (forty-six at the beginning) and the placing of the succeeding scene suggest that the deeper staging would be more practicable.

THE STAGING OF V.2. Before St. Edmund's Bury (180 lines cut to 95) (see Figure 16). If we assume that the preceding scene *was* set in the third grooves, the change to this one was produced by simply sliding on a pair of flats in the second grooves. It was customary to label the scene "The French Camp," and Kean's artists in 1858 provided a view of colorful tents. But in 1842 Telbin painted only a beautiful landscape consisting of large trees and abbey ruins in the foreground and a view of the city in the distance. After the gloomy stillness in which the preceding scene ended, the stage sprang vigorously to life with the flourishing of trumpets and the arrival of over forty actors representing the French forces, the English lords, Cardinal Pandulph and his suite, and the heroically defiant Bastard. The scene ended with flourishes of drums and trumpets, "Charges & Shouts swelling and decreasing" as the final battle got under way.

THE STAGING OF V.3. Battlefield near St. Edmund's Bury (17 lines) (see Figure 17). Ellis rather oddly labeled this picture "English Camp" in his notes on the water colors, and Kean's artists in 1858 painted another scene with tents. Telbin painted a colorful landscape with dead bodies in the foreground: this pair of flats came on in the first grooves (upper slot). "Alarums continue, louder and more faint." King John, consumed with fever, called for his litter, and set off toward Swinstead.

THE STAGING OF V.4. Battlefield near St. Edmund's Bury (61 lines cut to 48) (see Figure 18). As the noise of battle continued, another handsome landscape, showing a ruined windmill and other wreckage of war, was slid on in the first grooves (lower slot). The dying confession of Melun and the resolution of the English lords to return to King John brought the military action of the play to a close.

Shakespeare's V.5, which briefly shows the disasters of the French Dauphin, was cut out. Cues of "Ready at Lights" and "put Lights down" give warning of the important darkening of the stage for the next scene.

THE STAGING OF V.5 (*Folio*, V.6). Gate &c. of Swinstead Abbey (44 lines cut to 37) (see Figure 19). "Lamps down," Macready noted, to create a night effect, and this very handsome blue-black painting of a Gothic church and night sky was revealed in the first grooves (upper slot). The stage became deathly still, and Hubert, bearing a crossbow, crossed the stage three or four times "as if patrolling" before he challenged the Bastard, who was approaching from off stage left.

The critic of *John Bull* felt that the actors of the scene (Phelps and Anderson) had missed the point of it, and played it "as it were a 'carpenter's scene,' introduced solely to amuse the audience while the mechanist was 'setting the discovery.' " The following scene — the "discovery" — had of course been set during the entr'acte or during the battle scenes, and if the actors failed here to strike the "dreadful note of preparation" on the opening night, one hopes that they achieved it in subsequent performances.

THE STAGING OF V.6 (*Folio*, V.7). Orchard of Swinstead Abbey (118 lines cut to 77) (see Figure 20). The "abbey gates" flats were drawn away to reveal this deep scene of the abbey and its orchard, set in the fifth and sixth grooves. "Blue Mediums" were put on some of the lights to create a moonlight effect, and the "Floats" (footlights) were raised a little to increase visibility of the central part of the stage. The dying King John was brought in through "Abbey Gate Piece" in the third entrance right, lying on a couch borne by six monks. Four knights and nobles carried torches, and about seventeen others attended the King's death. The play ended with slow and solemn organ music from the church and a very slow curtain.

The fifth act, comprised of six scenes (of Shakespeare's seven), and reduced from 521 lines to 348, was played in twenty-eight minutes. Ellis usually recorded the time of the whole play (2,570 lines cut to 1,830) as "2 Hrs & 45 Min^{s} — includ^{g} waits," which breaks down into 2:27 of overture and playing time and eighteen minutes for the entr'actes. John Willmott penciled at the end of his prompt-book five separate timings, ranging from "2–50" down to "2–42." In any case the overall movement of the dialogue was "tragically" deliberate — the average progress of the verses being about twelve and a half per minute.

Figure 7. Act I, scene 1. Hall of State in King John's Palace (Macready)

Figure 8. Act II, scene 1. Before the Gates of Angiers (Macready)

Figure 9. Act III, scenes 1 and 4. Interior of French King's Tent (Macready)

Figure 10. Act III, scene 2. Battlefield Before Angiers (Macready)

Figure 11. Act III, scene 3. Another part of the battlefield (Macready)

Figure 12. Act IV, scene 1. Vaulted Apartment in Northampton Castle (Macready)

Figure 13. Act IV, scene 2. Hall of State (Macready)

Figure 14. Act IV, scene 3. Northampton Castle (Macready)

Figure 15. Act V, scene 1. Interior of Templars' Church (Macready)

Figure 16. Act V, scene 2. Before St. Edmund's Bury (Macready)

Figure 17. Act V, scene 3. Battlefield near St. Edmund's Bury (Macready)

Figure 18. Act V, scene 4. Battlefield near St. Edmund's Bury (Macready)

Figure 19. Act V, scene 5. Gate &c. of Swinstead Abbey (Macready)

Figure 20. Act V, scene 6. Orchard of Swinstead Abbey (Macready)

The Dramatis Personae
[from the playbill of October 24, 1842]

King John . . . . Mr. MACREADY
Prince Henry, his Son,
(afterwards King Henry the 3rd) . . . . Miss HOWARD
Arthur, Duke of Bretagne (*Son of Geffrey, late Duke of Bretagne, the elder brother of King John*) . . . . Miss NEWCOMBE
William Marshall, Earl of Pembroke . . . Mr. W. H. BLAND
Geffrey Fitz-Peter, Earl of Essex,
Chief Justiciary of England . . . . Mr. ELLIS
William Longsword, Earl of Salisbury . . . . . Mr. ELTON
Robert Bigot, Earl of Norfolk . . . . Mr. STANTON
Hubert de Burgh, (*Chamberlain to the King*) . . Mr. PHELPS
William Plantagenet, Earl of Warrenne . . . . . Mr. STILT
William, Earl of Arundel . . . . Mr. PAULO
Robert, Baron Fitz-walter . . . . Mr. CARLE
Bohun, Earl of Hereford . . . . Mr. GILBERT
Vere, Earl of Oxford . . . . Mr. BRADY
Robert de Ros . . . . Mr. KING
Richard de Percy . . . . Mr. PRIORSON
Gilbert de Clare . . . . Mr. LAKE
English Barons . . . . . . Messrs. HILL, JONES, CLARKE, THOMPSON, &c. &c.
Sheriff of Northampton . . . . Mr. HARCOURT
Knights . . . . Mr. HOWELL and Mr. YARNOLD
English Heralds . . . . . Mr. ROBERTS and Mr. SEYMOUR
Robert Faulconbridge
(*Son of Sir Robert Faulconbridge*) . . Mr. M. BARNETT
Philip Faulconbridge (*his half-brother, bastard Son to King Richard the 1st*) . . Mr. ANDERSON
Officers . . . . Mr. C. J. SMITH and Mr. JONES
James Gurney (*Servant to Lady Faulconbridge*) . Mr. SEVIER
Peter of Pomfret (*a Prophet*) . . . . Mr. MELLON
Archbishop, Bishops, Mitred Abbots, Monks, Esquires, Standard-Bearers, Attendants, &c.
Philip Augustus (*King of France*) . . . . . . Mr. GRAHAM
Lewis the Dauphin . . . . Mr. HUDSON
Arch-Duke of Austria . . . . Mr. SELBY
Giles, Vicomte de Melun . . . . Mr. G. BENNETT
Chatelain d'Arras . . . . Mr. SHARPE
Thibaud Count de Blois . . . . Mr. SMITH
Eustache de Neuville . . . . Mr. STRINGER
Chatelain de St. Omer . . . . Mr. BURDETT
Baldwin de Bretel . . . . Mr. ROFFEY
Bartholomew de Roye . . . . Mr. UPSDELL
Ralph de Beaumont . . . . Mr. J. ROFFEY
Chatillon, Count de Nevers
(*Ambassador from France to King John*) . . Mr. LYNNE
French Heralds . . . . . Mr. BENDER and Mr. WILKINSON
Cardinal Pandulph, the Pope's Legate . . . . . Mr. RYDER
Attendants on the Cardinal, Notarius Apostolicus, Crozier Bearer, Bishops, Monks, Knights-Templars, Gentlemen, &c.
Citizens of Angiers . . . . Mr. WALDRON
Messrs. HILL, MORGAN, ROWLAND, WALKER, GREENE, &c.
Knights-Hospitallers, Barons, Austrian Knights, Esquires, Trumpeters, Standard-Bearers, Attendants, &c. &c.
Queen Elinor, (*Widow of King Henry the 2nd, and Mother of King John*) . . . . Miss ELLIS
The Lady Constance, (*Mother to Arthur*) . Miss HELEN FAUCIT
Blanch, (*Daughter to Alphonso, King of Castile, & Niece to King John*) . . Miss FAIRBROTHER
Lady Faulconbridge, (*Mother to the Bastard & Robert Faulconbridge*) . . . . Mrs. SELBY
Ladies, — Mesdames SUTTON, TRAVIS, MARSANO, TRAVIS, LEE, CARSON, &c.

King John was performed twenty-six times during the season: October 24, 28, 31, November 4, 7, 11, 14, 18, 21, 23, 25, 28, 30, December 2, 5, 9, 12, 19, 28, January 2, 11, 18, 25, February 8, March 28, and May 15. There were very few changes of cast. As of November 4, Mr. Sevier disappeared from the role of James Gurney and was replaced by Mr. Hance. From January 2 on Miss Howard was replaced by Miss Gould in the role of Prince Henry. In the last two performances Mr. Mellon played Pembroke, Mr. S. Jones played Peter of Pomfret, and Mr. G. Bennett played Philip Augustus. In the last performance, Miss Webster played Blanch. On one occasion only (January 18), Mrs. Warner substituted for Helen Faucit in the role of Constance. Beginning on December 5 the names of some thirty-five of the minor characters were dropped to lower-case print, and from December 28 were eliminated from the playbill entirely in order to make room for the elaborate description of the Christmas pantomime.

The Acting

"Of the acting generally," said *John Bull,* "the method was far too violent. At the commencement the shouting would have warranted an opinion that Drury Lane was the training school for Richardson's booth. The noise was painful, and all possibility of delineation in such a tone prevented." Macready himself knows better, said the critic, and "is always audible because always distinct, and as he does not himself bellow forth all he utters, should, as director of this stage, strenuously check the inclination of the players to shout their parts." The *Athenaeum,* too, complained of the ranting and screaming, and pled for "a little regard for the ears of the audience, which are assailed in a most unmerciful manner by some of the performers." Perhaps, as *John Bull* dryly suggested, "all the actors were excited on the occasion of new clothes," and perhaps after the first performances the defect was moderated. Yet it could hardly have been reformed altogether, at least in the first four scenes of the play, for this "effect defective" plainly "came by cause": it was the inevitable result of Macready's effort to energize the opening scenes greatly so that the contrast before and after the dark transition (III.3) would be as strong as possible. Not everyone made the same complaint, however. The *Atlas* critic, indeed, found overall excellence of acting to be the hallmark of the production, and regretted the impossibility of even mentioning all the praiseworthy performances: "Good actors have been put into inferior parts, and have thereby made general goodness a feature in this new and improved version of *King John*. This is a double compliment to the unselfish zeal of the actors and to the virtuous sternness of a manager who, in spite of individual pretensions, dares to do fairly by his company and his audiences by making the former work, with a commonwealth disinterestedness, towards the glories of the national drama."

The roles usually singled out for analysis — praise or blame — were of course Macready's King John, Helen Faucit's Constance, James Anderson's Faulconbridge, Samuel Phelps's Hubert, and the Prince Arthur of the child actress, Miss Newcombe.

The character of King John had been Macready's study for many years. He had first played it during the 1822-23 season at Covent Garden Theatre (five times), just before he broke with Charles Kemble and the Covent Garden management and moved to Drury Lane. This, by the way, was the season *before* Charles Kemble's famous revival of *King John* for which J. R. Planché designed the costumes and superintended the stage management. At Drury Lane Macready played King John twice in the season of 1824-25, once in 1830-31, once in 1831-32, once in 1833-34, and once in 1835-36. He moved to Covent Garden in 1836-37, and played it there fourteen times. Thus he had played it (in London) twenty-five times before his own 1842-43 revival; he would play it twenty-six times during the revival, and four times more at the Haymarket during his farewell season in 1850.

When he first undertook the role, he tells us (*Reminiscences,*

1875, p. 211), he was very much aware of John Philip Kemble's great reputation as King John, which "had reference chiefly, if not exclusively, to the grand scene of John's temptation of Hubert. On this I bestowed, of course, my utmost pains, but brought also into strong relief that in which the coward monarch endeavours to shift his own criminality on Hubert, a scene to which Kemble, in his impressive representation of the part, had neglected to give prominence." He does not mention here the distinction usually noticed between Kemble's King John and his own: that the nobly Roman Kemble underscored the "kingliness" of the character, whereas Macready, who had fought his way into eminence in the London theatre through a dreary succession of Gothic villain roles, underscored the villainy. Herein lay Macready's important achievement, for, as Leigh Hunt would later declare, he was "more like the real historical King John, the vacillating, weak, wilful monarch, less poetical than petulant and a bully" (*Dramatic Essays,* 1894, p. 193).

From 1833 on, Macready's *Diaries* contain many records of his preparation and execution of the role. On December 5, 1833, four days before he was to perform it at Drury Lane, he began to restudy it, hoping desperately (for he was in the midst of what William Archer calls his "doldrum" years) that this — or Coriolanus or Sardanapalus — would be the role "to excite attention in." After rehearsal the next day he knew that he must probe it deeper, "for I am not master in execution of my own wishes . . . in the part, which I ought to act grandly." On December 7, "a very rainy and tempestuous day," he took the early morning coach home to his country place in Elstree and spent the hours from breakfast until four in the afternoon studying King John in his upstairs drawing room. December 9 was the performance. He was annoyed during the morning rehearsal because the actor of Hubert absented himself, and he was intensely annoyed about some mishap in the preparation of his costume, which it appears he had ordered new for the occasion. When evening came, "I went to the theatre, thinking first of my dress and secondly of King John! I am ashamed, grieved and distressed to acknowledge the truth: I *acted* disgracefully, worse than I have done for years. . . . I did what I feared I should do, sacrificed my character to my dress!!" His friends Talfourd and Wallace came to his dressing room afterwards, and "I felt what they thought of my performance; it has made me very unhappy." He was terrified of what the next morning's papers would say, and could not go to bed "from self-dissatisfaction." To his amazement the next morning the press was "very indulgent indeed," except that the Herald objected to his *costume*: "so that I suffered as I ought, but not in the degree I merited."

Though he played the part but this once in the season, some two months later there appeared in the *Monthly Repository* (February, 1834) a glowing essay about it, written by the actor-lecturer-critic Charles Reese Pemberton ("Pel. Verjuice"). Pemberton praised Macready unstintingly for the intensity and accuracy of his characterization, for "no tame yielding to the conceptions of predecessors in the part," for avoiding conventional elocution ("you would have *seen him think,* and heard him speak his thoughts"), for bringing out the essential meanness of King John and boldly abjuring the customary "appeals to a favorite Bullism — a swagger of independence and patriotism"; and he described with remarkable vividness nine or ten great passages of Macready's acting. When Macready read the essay on February 7 and 8, it only revived his shame. It was "too eulogistic," he noted. "His imagination lends me attributes not my own." Nonetheless Pemberton's essay must have been enormously useful to him in his future studies of the role.

Two seasons later, on April 19, 1836, he played it again at Drury Lane rather more to his own satisfaction. "Acted King John in a way that assured me that I could play it excellently; it seemed to make an impression on the house, but I had not made it sure, finished, and perfectly individualized." Two features of the evening were distressing. Mrs. Sharpe was "very ineffective in the effective part of Constance," because, Macready suggests, of her "common mind." And at the passage of defiance to the Pope (III.1.147-160), "some fools set up a montrous hubbub"; it was reported to Macready in the green room afterwards that the Catholics would "cut our throats." The next day's *Morning Post* slighted Macready and wrote up Mrs. Sharpe's Constance at length.

In the fall of 1836, Macready having removed to Covent Garden after his disastrous knock-down quarrel with Alfred Bunn, *King John* was revived by manager Osbaldiston and performed fourteen times during the season, with Charles Kemble as Faulconbridge and the novice Helen Faucit as Constance. One gathers it was not much of a production — "with some seven ragged supernumeraries for the power of England," as John Forster would afterwards remember it," while that of France, headed by a king in boots *à la* Louis Quatorze, crawled about the stage with three" (*Examiner,* October 29, 1842). No more was needed, though, to draw decent audiences. It was billed as Kemble's farewell season, and the public wanted to see their old favorite in one of his most distinguished roles; Macready's box-office value had risen, too, at cost of great shame to himself, because of his notorious exchange of fisticuffs with the execrable Bunn during the previous spring. In any case, however much he resented sharing the public's attention with an actor like Charles Kemble, of whom he was by no means fond, Macready could use the run of *King John* — the only extended one he had ever enjoyed — as an occasion for serious study. At the opening, on October 6, he was ill prepared and quite ashamed of himself. "If one has not made oneself master of character before the day of performance, it is not then to be done; all is chance, and raw, and wild — not artist-like. Acted King John in a style very much beneath myself — no identity, no absorbing feel of character." His dying scene, he thought, was his only good part. To his annoyance, the audience "called" for both Kemble and himself: "I do not fancy these duets." On October 31 he thought his performance went "tolerably well," and he hit upon a discovery in the role which he would not forget: "The second scene with Hubert [IV.2] better than before by taking *time* between the periods of passion." On November 10 he allowed himself a small meed of praise: "Acted much of King John — all but the scene of accusation against Hubert — very well indeed." On November 30 he again acted "tolerably well," but he noticed that Miss Faucit and Kemble received more applause than he. This he spitefully put down to the low mentality of the sort of audiences brought to the theatre by Osbaldiston's policy of low prices: "for they hail rant and roar with an ardent spirit of reciprocity."

The harassments of management during the autumn and winter of 1842-43, when he created his own production, prevented him from careful diarizing. There are no notes about his preparation and few about his performance of King John. On the opening night he wrote, "Acted King John fairly. Called for and very well received. Gave out the play. Serle, Dickens, Forster, Emerson Tennent, Stanfield, Maclise came into my room. All pleased." Thereafter occur only occasional notations of "tolerably well," "fairly," or "very well indeed." It was worth recording on November 1 that William Henry Murray, the respected manager of the theatres of Edinburgh, had called and "expressed himself delighted with the *perfect* representation of King John, observing that his 'master,' J. Kemble, had only 'made a step.' " Such a compliment from a confirmed Kembleite was to be treasured.

The responsible critics were agreed, in striking unanimity, that Macready's King John was "a fine personation," "the best which our modern stage is capable of producing," "not only one of his finest conceptions, but most perfect in execution." It is needless to repeat these generalized eulogies in detail. The interest of the critics' reports lies in their vivid descriptions of the salient sections and scenes of the character as Macready delivered it: John almost as hero-king, yet incipiently vicious, through Acts I, II, and half of III; John as coward-king and villain thereafter — notably in the temptation scene (III.3), the remorse scene (IV.2), and the final death scene. In the early part he was "grand and heroic," said the *Atlas*. He wore "the royal bearing and dignity with instinct and consummate art," said the *Illustrated London News*. "It was with the enthusiasm of chivalric valor that he flung himself into the midst of his barons, in the third act, and incited them to a defiance of France," said the *Times*. He was careful not to give the character away, so to speak, by too many signs of weakness or meanness in the early scenes. The critic of *John Bull* specifically marked this as an improvement over Macready's known manner in the part — that "in the earlier scenes more alacrity of spirit was depicted, as more in accordance with the velocity of John's earlier actions."

The energy, brightness, and bustle of the first part of the play were, as we have seen, deliberately calculated to prepare for the bold *coup de théâtre* midway in the third act. "If one portion of this great performance could be singled out without injustice to the rest," said *The Examiner*, "we would make special mention of the gloom and stillness which followed John's success in battle after the sudden defection of the French. What there is of the Plantagenet in John closes from that moment: its place is taken by mean cowardice, by miserable selfishness, by vacillating weakness: and with admirable truth was it shown upon the stage, that, like a lowering cloud, the change hangs over the tragedy to the end." The temptation scene was held by many to be the most remarkable passage of acting in the play. The *Times* critic reported that "It was a foreboding look that John cast on Arthur, the tongue faltered as the horrible mission was intrusted to Hubert. For a moment the countenance of the king beamed as he said 'Good Hubert,' but the gloom returned when he said 'Throw thine eye on yonder boy.' That he did not look Hubert in the face when he proposed 'death' was a fine conception." "His tempting of Hubert to murder Arthur," said the *Spectator*, "is a masterly exhibition of coward villainy; before a word is spoken you see the 'thought whose murder is fantastical' rising in his mind; conscience-stricken fear and doubt of Hubert's compliance alone delay its utterance; there is meanness alike in his cajolery and exultation." The *Atlas*, to be sure, accused him of lapsing here into "a striking sin of his style," of uttering his desires "gasping and spasmodic, as though he had done the deed he desires to have done, and was spirit-stricken, pouring forth the baleful secrets of his agonized soul."

The remorse scene, in which Macready claimed to have improved upon Kemble in the matter of shifting the blame from the King to Hubert, and which in 1836 he had learned how to strengthen "by taking *time* between the periods of passion," did not perhaps come off too well, at least on the opening night. The only critic I have noticed who singled out this scene for detailed comment objected to it as an alteration without improvement. According to *John Bull*, "Formerly Mr. Macready exhibited the King as humbled before the consciousness awakened by the fear of consequence. Every speech was thus connected, and the whole made one appeal, pleading the temptation by which he was surrounded against the accusation of having tempted. The passion thus rendered was more pathetic in its weakness, and more moral in its impression than when broken into pieces by delivery, some passages as though they were soliloquies, intended to be heard only by the audience."

The death scene was apparently an overwhelming exhibition of bodily agony. King John died from an excruciating poison, which, the play reports, made his official food taster's "bowels suddenly burst out." Macready's death was "surpassingly powerful," said the *Atlas*, who would "applaud to the echo so masculine and horrible a display" were it not for the fact that it went "beyond the truth required by the poet and the public." It was not for polite critics to approve quite so much "stress laid on the physically horrible."

The Lady Constance was played by Helen Faucit, who had first played it at Covent Garden in 1836 when she was but nineteen years old, and who now at twenty-five shared eminence with Mrs. Warner as the leading tragic actress in Macready's company. Statuesquely tall and very beautiful, Miss Faucit must have looked the part perfectly. She had never been physically strong, however, and recent illnesses had weakened her further, so that although she could fulfill the tenderer moments of the role, she was inadequate to its violences. Her husband, Sir Theodore Martin, tells us (*Helena Faucit,* 1900, p. 92) that after her "great cry of anguish, in which her grief culminates as she passes from the scene," she was generally carried fainting to her room. Almost every one of the critics remarked upon her lack of power, some indulgently, some unkindly. "Where there was so much earnestness, so much energy, so much passion as Miss Faucit displayed," said the *Times,* "we cannot help regretting to say that her Constance did not satisfy us. . . . There were rage, grief, irony, all well-intended; but still there seemed a constant effort to attain the unattainable." The *Atlas* noted that she was much applauded and deserved to be so: "What could be effected by energy, skill, and taste, she did; and if occasionally her burning words savoured a little of small scolding, more than of blighting execration, the want of such extra power leaves room only for regret." But the *Spectator* flatly rebuked her for having "overtasked her lungs in the mistaken effort to express mental anguish by physical violence" and called her first great scene "an exhibition of sheer impotence of rant to accomplish any greater feat than stunning the ears." *John Bull* cruelly and, I am sure, unfairly denied that she could even cultivate or control her imagination: "Her style is hard and her manner is violent. She mimics the grosser attributes of pain rather than depicts the finer emotions of grief, and hence she pains, very generally, but never affects, and her acting in Lady Constance . . . left an unpleasant conviction of the bodily suffering of some very noisy woman."

But Miss Faucit was to have a champion for her Constance before the season was over. In February, 1843, her enthusiastic admirer, George Fletcher, began to contribute to the *Athenaeum* a series of essays on Shakespeare, the first three of which were devoted to *King John.* Fletcher's essays, later collected in a volume called *Studies of Shakespeare* (1847), are very much concerned with Shakespeare on the stage, concerned especially with the playing of the women's roles, and ardently devoted to praise of the acting of Helen Faucit. (Ironically, the regular drama critic of the *Athenaeum* had dismissed Miss Faucit's performance with a sneering half-sentence that she "lets down the dignity of Queen Constance to the level of a scold.") In his "Introductory Essay," on February 4, as part of the exposition of the premises upon which the series is to be developed, Fletcher pays an initial tribute to Miss Faucit for having "shaken us with the passionate indignation, melted and thrilled us with the awfully beautiful despair, of Constance of Bretagne." In his second essay, on February 11, he sets about to disabuse his readers, including theatregoers, critics, and theatre personnel, of wrong-headed conceptions of the character of Constance which had been foisted upon them, first by Mrs. Siddons' acting of the role, second by Mrs. Jameson's well-known essay on Constance in her *Characteristics of Shakespeare's Women* (1832). Mrs. Jameson was wrong, he argues, in attributing to Constance "self-will and exceeding pride," "rashness," and "frantic violence of uncontrolled feeling." Mrs. Siddons wrongly thought her motivated by "ambition," made her too tigerlike, and resorted too much in her delivery to bitter sarcasm. In his third essay, on February 18, he devotes a dozen long paragraphs to Miss Faucit's way with the Lady. It is not *pride,* but *feeling,* that informs her rendering of the character. "She makes us feel throughout . . . the depth, the tenderness, and the poetry of the maternal affection, dwelling in a vivid fancy and a glowing heart." However majestic Mrs. Siddons may have been, she was deficient in this requisite tenderness and she failed to clear her brow of resentful scorn in passages addressed to the child Arthur; Miss Faucit, *between* her bursts of indignant reproach and fiery denunciation of her enemies, melts into double tenderness over the beauties and misfortunes of her child. Fletcher instances several passages of Constance's references to the princeling which were "exquisitely touching" and "indescribably sweet" in Miss Faucit's utterance; and he tells us how, when she threw herself to the ground at the climax of her grief (III.1.74), "she looks up, and raises her hand to play with the ringlets of her boy as he stands stooping over her." In the next passage, "the most difficult of all in so difficult a part," in which Constance rebukes King Philip and withers Austria with scorn, Fletcher is confident that Miss Faucit is far superior to Mrs. Siddons because the force she displays is not "the hard force of an arrogant, imperious termagant . . . but the *elastic* force that springs from a mind and person . . . so intellectual, so poetical, and so essentially feminine as that of Constance." She drew from her child's embrace and rose, as it were, "to more than the natural height of her noble figure," lifting her hands heavenward for the line "Arm, arm, you heavens, against these perjured kings." From this height, when she attacked the despicable Austria, "her piercing and scorching reproaches seem to be drawn down like the forked lightnings from above, searing and blasting where they strike." Her appeal to the Dauphin, "Oh, thine honour, Lewis, thine honour," was one of noble and generous fervor, not of sarcasm, as Siddons is reported to have rendered it. Fletcher declines rhetorically to elaborate on Constance's final despair scene (III.4). "The looks, and tones, and gestures . . . are not things to be described, but to be seen and heard, felt and wept over. For our own part, long shall we be haunted by those accents, now piercingly, now softly thrilling — now enamoured of Death, now rushing back to the sweet and agonizing remembrance of her child, now hurrying forward to anticipate the chasing of 'the native beauty from his cheek' — till her last lingering ray of hope expires, and reason totters on the verge of frenzy." In her last lines, Fletcher admits, her voice rises into a painful scream, but so it should, he says, for we should remember those lines painfully until retributive justice is brought home to her oppressors. Her exit from the play should not be a matter of "harmonious modulation," but "the death-shriek of a spirit violently departing."

It is difficult to assess Fletcher's essays, which treat also Miss Faucit's performing of Rosalind, Lady Macbeth, Juliet, Beatrice, and Imogen. One wants very much to believe that this beautiful young woman was really as discriminating, as sensitive, as imaginative, and as histrionically effective as Fletcher wills her to be. But he strains too hard. It may be that Mrs. Siddons' Constance was more formidable than loving; yet by her own testimony, as she sat in her dressing room night after night with the child beside her, her attention fixed on the "distressing events" of the scenes leading to her betrayal, the passions that rose in her and flooded her eyes with tears included *"above all,* the agonizing feelings of maternal affection." Mrs. Jameson, too, is emphatic enough on the theme of Constance's motherliness: indeed, Fletcher's rejection of Mrs. Jameson is a serious case of special pleading. Sir Theodore Martin tells us that Fletcher knew Miss Faucit personally and enjoyed many conversations with her on Shakespearean subjects: it would appear that the essays are in some measure a substitution of her drawing-room *persona* for her dramatic *persona.* The error is an amiable one.

James Anderson's Faulconbridge was not acceptable to most of the critics because it violated a deeply ingrained preconception (a quite false one) of how heroically the character ought to be played. It is true that by the end of the play the Bastard develops into a sort of hero. He picks up the reins of command as they slip from the enfeebled grasp of the King and converts his fierce energies to "the ordering of this present time." But certainly in the early scenes he is rather a comic roughneck than a hero. Shakespeare has taken his cue for the beginnings of the Bastard from that "hardy wild-head, rough and venturous" to whom Chatillon refers in the *Troublesome Raigne;* has rendered the Bastard loudmouthed, cynical, rude, and rackety — broadly humorous, of course — but insensitive, opportunistic, and with a strong propensity to billingsgate. The critics of the 1840's, however, wanted to idealize him, to have him hero all the way. They were still too close, perhaps, to the French wars, and certainly too full of memories of the "gentlemanly" Bastard of Charles Kemble, to allow the Shakespearean Bastard all his dimensions. "What a noble fellow is Falconbridge!," cried the *Times* critic. "He is the very personification of the dauntless courage and thorough-going fidelity of a rude age," etc., etc. *John Bull,* with less ingenuousness, actually *reasoned* him into gentlemanliness: "Faulconbridge comes from the country to the Court, but he comes thither the son of a King, bred a gentleman, and educated in the military exercises that at once fit him for the camp; his bearing might not be refined, but it would be chivalrous, naturally graceful, and in the kindness of his heart and inherent courage of his disposition, free from rudeness in expression or vauntingness in assertion. Mr. Anderson's manner to his mother . . . was devoid alike of respect and affection, and could not have otherwise than pained the parent whom Shakespeare depicts as being induced by it to make confession of her 'dear offence,' " etc.

No such milk-and-water dish was for James Anderson. From the tone of his own reminiscences (*An Actor's Life,* 1902), Anderson appears to have been a strappingly muscular, moderately rowdy young man, who took as much pleasure in pugilism and barroom brawls as in the histrionic art; whose life, apart from four seasons of loyal work under Macready, was a succession of ill-fated (and probably inartistic) ventures in theatrical management, terms in debtors' prison, and barnstorming tours in the provinces and abroad. A "hardy wild-head, rough and venturous," one might say — Faulconbridge to the life.

But not a Faulconbridge for the 1840's. *John Bull* thought that in the first three acts "his manner was coarse, his voice overstrained, and his action exaggerated." The *Athenaeum* wrote him down as "a swash-buckler hero." The *Times* thought that in the first act "the bluster was overdone, and the art of producing it not concealed." The *Spectator* thought he showed "too much of the bully and swaggerer" and declared outright that "Charles Kemble was the only modern actor equal to represent the physical grandeur and moral dignity of this noble specimen of valorous manhood."

The case is clear that these early Victorian observers thought they had found in the Bastard another flagbearer of national patriotism, another Henry V; they were shocked to be told by young Anderson that, hero though he was, the Bastard was also an unhousebroken rudesby. Quite possibly, of course, Anderson overdid it a bit, at least in the excitement of the opening night; but his conception of the part, or rather his instinct for it, was perfectly correct. And, happily, at least one voice emerged from the chorus of pained gentility to approve and praise him as he deserved to be praised. The critic of the *Atlas* wrote: "Mr. Anderson's Falconbridge is . . . a masterly performance. It leaves a great impression. It is, to our taste, more true to Shakspere than Charles Kemble's more smiling and polished effort. Bastard-born he even bastardizes heroism, and, bearing down before him all the actors in a stirring drama, amidst occasional snatches of caustic observation of men and manners, he surpasses all in the heroism of his grief over the body of his benefactor. All this Mr. Anderson draws with power and point. His loudness and vehemence, occasionally a fault, is here an 'observance.' " The *Atlas* got it right.

Samuel Phelps's Hubert was "very ably, quietly, and excellently sustained," said the *Literary Gazette,* which ranked his performance next after Macready's in excellence. "We never saw so good a Hubert as Mr. Phelps," said the *Examiner*: "his rough pathos was of heart-growth, and went straight to the hearts of all." The *Illustrated London News* credited him with enhancing Macready's own success, "for a better Hubert could not be found to 'play up to' the timidly-seducing monarch." "An actor with more manly pathos than any on the stage," said the *Times,* "he managed his pathos with great skill. The silent dejection when first Arthur was confided to his care was a presage of coming ill; the heavings of the heart while he strove to be stern to the innocent child showed the increasing struggle which was going on, till at last all resolved itself into the burst of tears at the words, 'I will not touch thine eyes,' which was the most powerful appeal to the sympathies of the audience throughout the piece." His "rugged aspect, voice, and manner, and the melting tenderness encased in that rough rind," said the *Spec-*

tator, "fit him for the part . . . and he becomes it well: there is a sternness in his very relenting; his fierceness is the resolution of a determined character, faithful to his royal master in all but crime." *John Bull* caviled that Phelps "rather suited the character to himself than got out of himself into the character," but forgave him on the grounds that

our actors, one and all, seem to have lost the ability to personate. . . . Some portions of his acting were delicately true. The strong man and hardened adventurer sinking prostrate before the better feelings of our nature was beautifully painted by him in the lines

Well, see to live; I will not touch thine eyes
For all the treasure that thine uncle owes.

The quiet pathos he expressed drew forth such appeals as perhaps induced Mr. Phelps to indulge in a more vehement style, for he concluded the scene with more noise than was effective, especially in his case, who is always best when not declaiming. Thus, for instance, his subdued but hearty repudiation of Arthur's murder was in its quietness powerful, and led beautifully to the regret he threw into the words "I left him well." When he can thus delineate the finest impulses we shall never pardon his adopting the hollow tricks of the stage, in the hope to make the vulgar clap their hands.

The child actress who played Prince Arthur, a Miss Newcombe, seems to have brought off the blinding scene with Hubert reasonably effectively. The *Athenaeum* allows her to have done it "very intelligently" and speaks in praise of "the domestic quality" which she gave to her expression of fear. She was "a pretty, interesting little child," said the *Times,* "with a voice somewhat of the highest, and with much feeling both in expressing grief and playfulness." "A most earnest and passionate little creature," the *Examiner* called her, "whose downright energy gave new terrors and new beauties to the master-scene." "Childish in grief and terror," said the *Literary Gazette,* "she accomplished a striking improvement on the usual recitative way in which the dialogue has been parrotted." That she was "overtrained," and might have been more natural with "somewhat less drilling" was an objection raised in several quarters; and the *Spectator,* who found her clever and touchingly simple in the main, rather sharply reveals in what direction her overtraining had led her: "The scene with Hubert is almost too painful: but she has been taught to give vent to her distress with the tearful dread of a child fearing bodily pain, rather than with that deeper-seated terror of the loss of sight which the language of the poet expresses." *John Bull* put it down as simply a matter of too much loudness: "Even the child . . . was falsely tutored to scream like the rest, and the little soul strained her voice in such a manner, that it was only toward the conclusion when, from exhaustion, she among the rest was compelled to resort to a less forced intonation, we discovered that her natural tone, though small, was sweet and pleasing." The blinding scene, *John Bull* thought, was a mistake in taste, in which "reality is sought and poetry sacrificed." The child was "made to kick and scream, and in the turbulence of infantine terror to banish the sweetness and beauty of the poet. It was a painful exhibition, and as it was lowered to the actual, became at last revoltingly effective. Such sights are natural to no dramatic purpose, and ought not to be introduced into the scenes of 'gentle Shakespeare.' "

Charles Kean's Productions of *King John*

Since the story of Macready's *King John* depends so much upon evidence from the documents and doings of Charles Kean, we must turn to Kean's productions of the play and ascertain what use he made of the materials in question and to what effect.

Charles and Ellen Kean spent the two seasons, 1845-47, in America. During the first season they were mainly engaged under the management of Edmund Simpson at the Park Theatre in New York City, occasionally punctuating their run with excursions to neighboring cities, and in the spring to the South and Middle West. They exhibited, to begin with, a stock repertory of about twenty pieces, from Shakespeare, Kotzebue, Colman, Tobin, Knowles, Talfourd, Bulwer, and the like (Odell's *Annals of the New York Stage,* 1931, V). In January, 1846, Kean brought out at the Park an impressive historical reconstruction of *Richard III,* which played nightly for three weeks and was enthusiastically acclaimed by the critics. Apparently by this time he had formulated a plan to treat the New York audiences to a systematic program of classical revivals. He had, it seems, commissioned George Ellis, the Drury Lane prompter, to provide him prompt-books of the master productions in the library of Drury Lane Theatre, and beginning about January, 1846, these began to arrive.

Early in the fall of his second season, on October 6, 1846, he introduced for the first time on any stage in America Shakespeare's *Two Gentlemen of Verona.* For this production Ellis had sent him a copy of Macready's prompt-book and ink drawings of the eight scenes as Macready had staged them. Historians are impressed by this event, but the New York audiences of the day were not, and the *Two Gentlemen* soon disappeared. On November 16, after endless preparations, enormous expense, and generous fanfare of press announcement, he opened *King John,* for which again Ellis had provided him with Macready's prompt-book and the scene designs of William Telbin. This too failed to draw, and it closed after a mere eighteen performances. Kean was so angered at the audiences' lack of appreciation that after the second night, as he wrote to Sol Smith, the St. Louis manager, he wanted to "address the audience on the subject & at once withdraw the piece" (*Letters of Mr. and Mrs. Charles Kean,* edited by W. G. B. Carson, 1945, p. 66). By the end of the run he had not only given up his intention "to produce a series of these revivals," but had quarreled with Simpson. The Keans abruptly seceded from the Park and from New York City, chastened in their expectations of Brother Jonathan's appetite for intellectual entertainment, and several thousands of dollars out of pocket for their experiment. Reverting to their stock repertory, they engaged with Noah Ludlow and Sol Smith and went off again on a tour of the South and Middle West. They returned to England in the summer of 1847. Just before the collapse of their New York engagement, the critic of the *Albion,* J. W. S. Hows, lamented that the New York audiences' indifference to *King John* was to deprive them of "the gratification of seeing 'Macbeth' and Milton's 'Comus,' produced with an equal attention to scenic and stage effects." Such specific knowledge of Kean's frustrated plans could only have come from Kean himself. We now know (see p. 13) that Kean had copies of Macready's prompt-books of *Macbeth* and *Comus* in store.

One can see why the facilities of New York's Park Theatre, or "Old Drury," could have tempted Kean to the dream of recreating there the recent triumphs of London's Drury Lane. The Park, like Drury Lane, was a huge house. As reconstructed in 1821, it seated some 2,500 persons. Its stage dimensions were very similar to those of Drury Lane: the proscenium opening was thirty-eight feet wide and twenty or twenty-one feet high, the stage depth was seventy feet, the width eighty feet. Its stock scenic equipment included, according to an inventory of 1828, fifty-nine pairs of flats, 188 wings, 400 pieces of set scenery, ten drop scenes, and so on (Odell's *Annals of the New York Stage,* III, 1-4, 58, 317, etc.). Although by 1846 the fortunes of the Park were seriously declining, the theatre's physical arrangements were perfectly accommodated to the most elaborate of Drury Lane stagings — *King John* among the rest.

From Kean's prompt-book we see how nearly he followed Macready's text and ground plans. Comparison of his costume notes with those of J. R. Planché reveals that like Macready he used Planché's historical evidence for the costumes. There were 176 costumes made new for the occasion, so the playbill informs us — a somewhat larger number, I compute roughly, than Macready used. Even so, Kean must have augmented the new costumes from the stock wardrobe of the Park, for he employed an enormous band of supernumeraries. In the second scene alone, according to the

Albion review of November 21, "there cannot be less than two hundred persons engaged." The *New York Herald,* in an anticipatory notice on the day of the opening, says that Kean had been drilling the supernumeries for the last six weeks, that they numbered 150 or 200, and that they were chosen for "superiority in education and ability." Nettled by the pretentiousness of such claims, the author of the humor sheet *Yankee Doodle* spoke sarcastically of the "five or six or seven hundred supernumeraries"; and on November 21 explained that "THE SILENCE IN THE STREETS In the mornings now, is entirely owing to the performance of King John at the Park, — all the fish-men and ash-cart men having been engaged by Mr. Kean as trumpeters to the 'borrowed Majesty of England.' One of them, in a fit of professional absence of mind, immediately after having executed his flourish before the walls of Angiers and the combined armies of England and France, cried out — 'Porgies!' "

The main question which begs attention is to what extent Kean used — reproduced or improved upon — the Telbin scene designs. We may be sure at least that Kean's staging fell nothing short of Telbin's model in terms of pictorial splendor. "No labor or expense has been spared," said the playbill, "in endeavoring to attain the utmost of historic illustration." Even before the production opened, the expenses had exceeded $12,000 (*Spirit of the Times,* November 14), and near the close of the run the *Herald* reported that Kean had sunk "$8,000 at least, of his private fortune" in the venture. "The scenery is entirely new, from accredited authorities," said the *Albion* on November 14, "and the artists at the Park have most ably performed their tasks." The playbill tells us that the scenes were "painted on upwards of 15,000 square feet of canvas by Mr. Hillyard, Mr. Grain, and Assistants." This acreage of canvas gives us something to work with, and the figure sounds about right. Analysis of Telbin's sets, based on the known dimensions of flats and wings at Drury Lane, plus rough computation of the dimensions of the set pieces and borders, produces a figure between 15,000 and 16,000 square feet of surface. Kean's sets were comparable to Macready's in extensiveness.

Few of the New York papers of the time, unfortunately, devoted much space to theatricals, so that it is not easy to find descriptive accounts of *King John* sufficiently detailed to assure us what the staging actually looked like. Such points as do come through, however, suggest close correspondences to Telbin's designs. As we have seen, during the week before Kean's production opened, Epes Sargent published with the acting edition of the play some notes from the London *Examiner* and *Spectator* describing the Drury Lane production. These, Sargent says, are "equally applicable to the style in which it is to be put upon the stage at the Park." The phrase "to the style in which" is cautiously vague; but any wonder about Sargent's intention is dispelled by the fact that five days *after* the opening, the *Spirit of the Times* copied this whole passage into its own review, calling it "perfectly descriptive," and asserting that it "applies as accurately to the piece, at the Park, as it could to the piece at Drury Lane."

Sargent quotes enough to illuminate the first two scenes — King John's throne room and the embattled walls of Angiers. Of the throne room the telling words about the Drury Lane production are: "the Gothic hall being hung with tapestry, but above showing the bare stone walls, adorned with only a square canopy over the chair of state, and the carved timbers of the roof." In the *Albion* of November 21, J. W. S. Hows, describing the throne room at the Park, speaks of "a vast Gothic Hall hung with tapestry. The carved timbers of the roof, stretching out in the perspective with the lights and shades skilfully arranged, the double range of windows of painted glass, the canopied chairs of state. . . ." Surely Hows and the London reviewer were looking at much the same stage picture, and it is the picture of Telbin's design. Kean appears to have added one prominent embellishment to the scene: Hows speaks of the "tesselated pavement," and the *New York Herald* of November 20 tells us that the floor was "covered with a cloth, on which are designed the royal arms of England, surmounted by the cross." In the second scene, according to Sargent's notes from London, "the chivalry of France and England, arrayed in the glittering panoply of war, meet before the gates of Angiers; the lofty ramparts and bastions of the town, stretching out in dim perspective along the river's bank frown defiance on the rival forces." At Drury Lane, too, as we have seen, the French camp was indicated on the first three wings at stage right, and the scene was "A Set to 7th Grooves." In Hows's New York report in the *Albion,* "the walls of Angiers, with a panoramic view of the French camp and adjacent country . . . is a splendid effort of pictoral art, occupying the entire depth, and a greatly increased breadth of stage. The lofty ramparts, bastions and towers, stretching out into the perspective, and the surrounding country, are depicted with great beauty and artistic skill." Then again comes the Kean embellishment: "Rude engines of war, block houses for covering the huge battering rams, and machinery for hurling ponderous stones, are introduced." Perhaps it was because of these tesselated pavements and engines of war that Hows was moved, "on the testimony of high authority," to declare of the staging "that in one or two scenes, it has never been excelled in any theatre in Europe."

The innovations contributed to an embarrassment in stage management, however. It was impossible to change from the first act set to the second in the customary entr'acte time. At Drury Lane the shift had been made in a miraculous five minutes. At the Park it took fourteen minutes on some occasions, and perhaps on the opening night even longer. Kean apologized in his curtain call address, and promised that such delays would not occur again (*Herald,* November 17). But subsequent playbills "respectfully solicited" the audiences' indulgence between the first and second acts, pointing out, among other herculean labors to be performed, one which I do not at all understand, that the stage had to be "thrown open to the walls of the theatre." *Yankee Doodle,* of course, got his bit of mean fun out of the embarrassment. "THE TIME Which elapsed between the first and second acts of King John was, with reason, thought to be the longest interval of nothing ever known; but that which Mr. Kean took to glower upon poor little Arthur, before asking Hubert to cut his throat, was found still longer, and even this was outstretched by the deliberation with which Mr. Kean points out 'A gra-a-a-a-a-a-a-a-ve' to Hubert as the proper receptacle for his little cousin. It has been supposed, that to keep up the fidelity of the scene, the Sexton of Trinity Church is engaged to dig a grave within the flats while Mr. Kean utters this word. We doubt this. He could do it in half the time if he were in any sort of practice." The total of "waits" at the Park sometimes took up to forty minutes, as against eighteen at Drury Lane.

The staging of the first scene of the third act corresponds to Telbin's design, according to Hows's report in the *Albion*: "a view of the interior of the French King's tent, and the town of Angiers seen in perspective through the opening." In the blinding scene (IV.1), according to the prompt-book, the "Door in Flat" was eliminated from the back wall and moved to the second entrance right: this probably implies a newly designed setting. The scene of Arthur's leap from the tower (IV.3) "is a scene beautifully painted. The fall of the young prince from the lofty battlements is managed with thrilling effect." We know from the prompt-book that the staging of this scene was reversed from Telbin's design, the battlements being at stage right. The scene of King John's submission to Pandulph (V.1), "commences with a view of the Temple Church, Northampton." As we have seen, this setting was a Macready-Telbin invention, the scene having previously been played in a "room in the palace." The final scene was surely a reproduction of Telbin's design. Hows wrote that it was, perhaps, "the most perfect specimen of scenic art ever exhibited in this country. It represents the orchard of Swinstead Abbey by moonlight. The Abbey, lit up as for High Mass, occupies the background. Here the dying King is brought in . . . the organ swells in solemn strains from the Abbey church." The *Herald* reported on November 20 that "On one side rise the gloomy walls of the monastery, from the gate of which issues a train of monks and nobles, bearing the couch of the dying monarch"; and from the church attached to the abbey is seen "the light of torches gleaming through its stained windows." Of the remaining scenes, including the five landscape or battlefield scenes, I can find no details in New York papers.

On February 9, 1852, Kean produced *King John* in London — his "first *great* attempt," as J. W. Cole tells us, in his long program of historical reproductions of the classic drama at the Princess's Theatre. The playbills credit three painters for the scenes: Mr. Dayes for I.1, IV.2, IV.3; Mr. Gordon for II.1, III.3, V.3, V.4, V.6; and Mr. Lloyds for III.1 and 4, III.2, IV.1, V.1, V.2, V.5. To what extent the scenes were new conceptions or to what extent they were adapted from Telbin's old designs, it is quite impossible to say, for by 1852 the London critics' reports had markedly diminished from the generous essays of a decade earlier, and except for remarks on the actors and the acting they had mostly become mere "notices." The *Times,* to be sure, called the production "one of the most complete representations known in the history of theatrical management"; the *Spectator* said that "the mounting is so very complete . . . it may fairly be considered a new work of art"; the *Athenaeum* declared that Kean had surpassed both Macready and Phelps in "magnificence." I can find only one picture of the production, a sketch of the blinding scene (IV.1) in the *Illustrated London News* of April 17, 1852: it clearly reverted to Telbin's original (which Kean perhaps abandoned in 1846), showing the same off-center "Door in Flat" at the back, the same curtained opening in the first entrance left, and very similar table, column, and Gothic vaulting.

When Kean revived *King John* on October 18, 1858, as a feature of his farewell season, the critics had even less to say about the scenic arrangements. Afterwards, however, Kean caused his prompter T. W. Edmonds to make up a finished prompt-book of the production, with water colors of the scene designs inserted (now at the Folger) and then too or soon thereafter caused someone to make another set of very similar water colors (now at the Victoria and Albert). By this time Telbin himself was one of Kean's chief painters, along with Thomas Grieve; Messrs. Gordon, Lloyds, and Dayes were listed only as assistants. I do not know whether the scenery for the 1858 *King John* was painted new or was the 1852 scenery brought out of storage. But in any case we can examine the water colors, compare them with Telbin's originals, and thus measure the Telbin "influence" (see Figures 21 to 34).

Because Kean was still following Macready's text and stage direction, it follows that the ground plans of the scenes — the location of the main entrances and the disposition of furniture — remained nearly everywhere the same. Other factors, however, militated for change. Kean could not have exactly reproduced Telbin's old designs for London audiences, as I think he had nearly done for New York audiences, without danger of hostile notice. The Princess's Theatre was much smaller than Drury Lane and its stage less generous in all dimensions, so that there was not room for the largest of the 1842 scenes in full scale. And Kean was by now wholly overmastered by his passion for historical accuracy — in this case to base everything upon "specific remains of the twelfth and thirteenth centuries" (*Preface* to the souvenir edition). Thus, for instance, King John's room of state (I.1, Figure 21) is a wholly new design. Perhaps the Princess's stage had not the height to afford the gorgeously soaring hammerbeam arches of Telbin's original: in any case, the 1858 ceiling appears to be quite flat, resting upon perfectly straight beams, and the room as a whole is a rather ordinary cube, the walls being broken by numerous arched doors and high windows. In his *Preface* Kean tells us that the room "is copied from the Hall in Rochester Castle." And indeed it does reproduce something of the shape and decor of the still discernible "room of state" in the ruined keep at Rochester, especially in the large side openings divided by cylindrical columns and topped by round arches with zigzag decorations.

Figure 21. Act I, scene 1. Hall of State in King John's Palace (Kean)

Figure 22. Act II, scene 1. Before the Gates of Angiers (Kean)

Figure 23. Act III, scenes 1 and 4. Interior of French King's Tent. (Kean)

Figure 24. Act III, scene 2. Battlefield Before Angiers (Kean)

Figure 25. Act III, scene 3. Another part of the battlefield (Kean)

Figure 26. Act IV, scene 1. Vaulted Apartment in Northampton Castle (Kean)

Figure 27. Act IV, scene 2. Hall of State (Kean)

WILLIAM CHARLES MACREADY'S
King John

Figure 28. Act IV, scene 3. Northampton Castle (Kean)

Figure 29. Act V, scene 1. Interior of Templars' Church (Kean)

Figure 30. Act V, scene 2. Before St. Edmund's Bury (Kean)

Figure 31. Act V, scene 3. Battlefield near St. Edmund's Bury (Kean)

Figure 32. Act V, scene 4. Battlefield near St. Edmund's Bury (Kean)

Figure 33. Act V, scene 5. Gate &c. of Swinstead Abbey (Kean)

Figure 34. Act V, scene 6. Orchard of Swinstead Abbey (Kean)

The scenery for the second act, before the gates of Angiers (Figure 22), at once imitates the 1842 design in effect and simplifies it in stage depth. Whereas the 1842 scene was "A Set to 7th Grooves," Kean's probably went no deeper than the fifth grooves. The gate and tower units at stage left are boldly painted and obviously had to be three dimensional. But the farther portions of the castle walls and towers, colored more faintly, were probably painted on the same back cloth as the sky, the distant mountains, and the French camp on the plains below. An engine of war fills up the stage right portion of the design.

The interior of the French King's tent (III.1 and 4, Figure 23) is obviously derived from Telbin's original. Through the same opening at the back (but larger and more prettily draped) we see again the tents of the French camp and beyond them the castle of Angiers on the hilltop (Figures 24 and 25). Telbin's original side posts hung with armor and his brown coloring of the tent ceiling have been dispensed with: the whole interior is painted bright blue with red and gold border trimmings. The castle room for the blinding scene (IV.1, Figure 26) again imitates Telbin's original, though it has been made more symmetrical and the Gothic vaulting of the ceiling is more regularized. The door at the back has been placed dead center and set at the top of a short stairway (an innovation since 1852): whereas in 1842, and probably in 1852, the door was a "door in flat" at left center, the 1858 door and stairs is apparently a "set piece" inserted into the opening of a "cut flat" exactly where the two halves of the flat come together. The throne room (IV.2, Figure 27) resembles Telbin's original insofar as the back wall is decorated by three round arches. These are equal in size, however, and there is no center opening showing a vista of a farther hall. Above the arches are tiny windows. There is no indication of a beamed ceiling. The exterior of Northampton Castle (IV.3, Figure 28), with the tower for Arthur to leap from, is moved from stage left to stage right, as it had been in the New York production. The tower and farther reaches of the castle are painted in light colors as if bathed in sunshine. The low round tower and archway in the foreground, painted in dark colors as if in shadow, are practically a mirror image of the 1842 arrangements. The Templars' Church (V.1, Figure 29) is very similar to that of 1842, except that five pointed arches are substituted for the original six round arches. The last two scenes — without and within the orchard of Swinstead Abbey (V.5 and 6, Figures 33 and 34) — are wholly different from Telbin's originals: Telbin's romantic architectural masses in Gothic manner have been replaced by lower buildings crowned with pepperpot roofs — far less mood-provoking but perhaps more correct for archeological reasons.

The battlefield and camp scenes (III.2 and 3, V.2, 3, and 4), all of which are simply a "picture" on a "pair of flats," show marked differences. Where Telbin originally tended merely to paint beautiful landscapes, the 1858 designs go in emphatically for tented encampments and other paraphernalia of war. The tents in V.2 and 3 are especially striking in color and "medieval" in design. Yet even in these battlefield scenes there are elements in common. The rocky hill of Angiers in the distance and an abandoned spear in the right foreground are present in both versions of III.2. Both versions of III.3 are dominated by stormy sky. The 1842 windmill in V.4 appears, differently treated, in the later III.3. War-ravaged trees, pools of water, dead bodies, and smashed war equipment are variously repeated from one set of designs to the other.

The most obvious overall difference between the 1842 and the 1858 designs is the palette from which they are painted. All of Telbin's original dark blues and blacks, dark browns, grays, and olive-greens have given place to bright browns, tans, reds, yellows, bright blues, and bright greens. The effect of the later designs, on paper, is harsh and unfeeling; but presumably the brighter palette communicated much better under the stage lights of the time.

It is difficult in this discussion of Kean's productions of *King*

John to avoid the imputation that Kean was not only surreptitious but downright unscrupulous in his procurement and use of Macready's production plans. And, as a matter of fact, Kean was notorious for such manipulations. In *Players and Playwrights* (1888, I, 78-80), John Coleman tells us that whenever Macready made a great hit in London, as in *The Lady of Lyons* or *Money,* Kean would so swiftly "anticipate" him with these plays in the provinces that Macready could not profitably tour them. When Macready got up *Sardanapalus* in 1834, Kean "by some sharp practice" obtained a prompt-book of it and took it to (of all places) Bristol, where Macready's own stepmother was the manageress. There was never much love lost between these relatives-by-marriage; but when, after the last night of the Bristol run, Kean asked the old lady what Macready would have to say about his doing *Sardanapalus,* she gave him a proper answer: "What do I think Mr. Macready will say when he hears of your doing 'Sardanapalus'? My good young man, I don't think Mr. Macready is aware of your existence!" In Kean's defense it must be acknowledged that there were no recognized property rights in prompt-books and production plans, and that such "borrowing" and "anticipating" were simply the theatrical jungle law of the time. Kean sometimes felt more sinned against than sinning. He actually believed, so Coleman tells us, that once when he was about to do *The Gamester* at the Haymarket, Macready anticipated *him* by bring it out at Drury Lane, knowing perfectly well that his own performance of Beverley would fail, and then caused his friends of the press "to slate the piece, stating that it was old-fashioned, bombastic rot, which even his genius couldn't galvanize into life." It may also be pointed out in Kean's defense that his New York production of *King John* was well outside Macready's "territory," and that he did not produce it in London until after Macready had retired. Further, we should note that Epes Sargent's introduction to the *Modern Standard Drama* edition of the play, which Kean must have approved of, gave Macready full credit for the arrangement of the acting version. In such matters it is not easy to draw the line between "thievery" and "carrying on the tradition."

The Prompt-Book: Notes to the Reader

The prompt-book here reproduced is not the prompt-book by which John Willmott (or George Ellis) guided the performances of Macready's *King John* at Drury Lane Theatre in 1842 and 1843. I have elected rather to present George Ellis' transcription of Macready's book which was used by Charles Kean in 1846 for his famous production of *King John* at the Park Theatre in New York City. The bulk of the notations, in George Ellis' distinctive hand, report the details of Macready's original creation. The additions, alterations, and strike-outs in the hands of the New York prompters prove Kean's use of the book.

George Ellis' calligraphy is a miracle of elegance and consistency, and when one becomes accustomed to a certain few of its idiosyncrasies it may be read with ease. Ellis seems to have used a fine but flexible nib, with the result that his long vertical strokes, as in the letters *l, h, t, b,* are often rather faint, and his horizontal strokes are comparatively bold. The connective strokes between the letters of a word are often omitted or appear only as a dot. He is much addicted to tiny dashes, and in emphatic passages every comma is followed by a dash. His capital *C* and capital *E* look almost identical, and both resemble his small *b,* all three consisting of a slender upper loop and a short fat lower loop connected by a curving vertical stroke: the one distinction is that the *E* always has a dot in the upper loop (see, for example, at the first page of Act I the *C*'s in the words *Copy, Cut, Charles, DeClare, Chatillon;* the *E*'s *in Esq*^{r}, *Ellis, Essex, E Heralds*). His double *s,* as in *Essex,* consists of an old-style long *s* followed by a modern short *s.* His capital *W* (see *DeWarrenne*) looks like a capital *H* with an extra outside stroke flying up to the right. His ampersand looks like a longhand capital

J, and it often appears with a small *c* to spell *et cetera.* He economizes with the expectable abbreviations of the time. The final letters or syllables of a word are often represented by a raised letter: *Esq*^{r} for *Esquire, disc*^{d} for *discovered, Mit*^{d} for *Mitered, beh*^{d} for *behind, immed*^{y} for *immediately, Q*^{n} for *Queen, adv*^{s} for *advances;* or by an apostrophe: *North'* for *Northamptonshire, Elin'* for *Elinor, Phil'* for *Philip, DeWar'* for *DeWarrenne.* He uses the traditional letter and number symbols to denote stage positions: *L* means *stage left, R* means *stage right, C* means *center stage, U* means *toward the back of the stage* (upstage). *E* or *Ent* means *entrance,* the numerals *1* to *7* refer to the grooves or entrances numbered from the front to the back of the stage. These letters and numbers occur in easily translatable combinations, as *L1E* (first entrance left), *RUE* (upper entrance right), *UC* (upstage center), and so forth. He *never* uses the then habitual but quite superfluous *H* (hand) in his directions. Whenever the reader discovers *LH* (to the left hand of the actor), *RH2E* (second entrance to the right hand of the actor), and the like, he will understand the direction to be an addition by a New York prompter, not a notation by Ellis. *Gr* means *groove. X* means *cross the stage,* and it occurs not only in its pure form but in such obvious compounds as *X'es, X'ing,* and *a'X* (across).

Certain technicalities of prompt-book notation which were more or less standardized in the nineteenth century should be carefully noted.

1. *Groove numbers.* At the head of each scene Ellis has recorded the groove or grooves in which slid the flats and wings (*5 G*^{r}*., A Set to 7th Gro*^{s}*., 3 & 5 Gr.*), and so on. These notations are suggestive but very sparse. In his "carpenter's notes," interleaved in the separate volume of scene designs, he has been much more specific about the scenic arrangements.

2. *Call lists.* At the head of each act, under a boldly inscribed number *one,* is a list of all the characters who are to be ready for the beginning of the act, with their stage properties if they are to carry any. As the act proceeds, further numbered call lists for later characters are posted well in advance of their entrances. These call lists were transcribed onto long slips, often made up into tall narrow booklets, which the callboy carried about to summon the actors from the green rooms.

3. *Key marks.* When stage directions were written on interleaves, as in this prompt-book, they were keyed to the text by a variety of symbolic marks. Circles, squares, crosses, triangles, variously dotted or crisscrossed, occur in prompt-books of the time. Ellis has confined himself to but three marks: a circle crossed vertically, a circle crossed diagonally, and a circle center-dotted.

4. *Sound effects.* Ellis has regularly marked sound effects with a set of three double crosses, like musical sharps.

5. *Stage maps.* Many of the most elaborate stage groupings are recorded in carefully annotated maps, showing the exact position of every character on the scene. These are of extraordinary value. From them, together with the given scene designs and costume designs, we can easily reconstruct the total picture as it existed. From them, too, we derive an immense respect for the discipline of the stage under the mid–nineteenth-century managers of the greater theatres.

6. *Bells and whistles.* Several boldly inscribed warning signals require translation. *RMB* tells the prompter to "ring music bell" — that is, to tinkle a bell which alerted the orchestra to ready itself for the entr'acte music. *RING* means to ring the bell which called for lowering the curtain at the end of an act. At the sound of this second bell, the orchestra, already alerted, would begin to play. In some prompt-books, though not this one, the end of the act is marked by *AD* (act drop). At the end of scenes *within* the acts the regular symbol is a *W,* that is, *whistle*: at the prompter's whistle the carpenters (stage hands) thrust on or drew off flats and wings to effect an instantaneous change of scene.

The additions and alterations imposed upon the prompt-book by Kean and his New York assistants, though numerous, are for the most part of minor significance, except where they reveal textual changes, revision of scenic arrangements, new "business," and records of the playing time. The entries were made by more than one hand, some in ink and some in pencil. It is not possible in photographic reproduction to capture the nuances of these additional notes — indeed, nothing short of direct examination of the book itself can satisfy the final questions of the expert investigator. I can here call attention only to some of the obvious features.

There is one bold, clear hand, whose notations are in ink and are evidently authoritative and final: perhaps Kean himself made these. By this hand is entered, opposite the page of "Persons Represented," the boxed notation of "Average Time at Park Theatre 1846" (a retrospective entry); and the second "call list" at page 196. Probably the same hand altered the numbers of attendant figures in the call list at page 193, added "2 Pages," translated "Cross" into "Silver Crozier." Throughout the book there are similar small tamperings with the call lists and stage maps, minor reversals of *R* and *L,* and revised placing of trumpeters from stage to orchestra and vice versa. The same hand probably added "going down" at page 208; "Adv LC to Blanch" at page 224; "P B" (Pandulph's Banner?) at page 231; the textual expansion "lost, lost," at page 244; "Pandulph retires up" and "RH1E" at page 246; "Borders down" at page 249 and all the corrective marks at this page and following to eliminate the "Door in Flat" and move it to "2 ERH"; "sitting on Stool L of chair" at page 250; "on stool, leaning on him" and "gets down LH" at page 251; "Kneels," "starts up," "goes up to fire," "down LH," and "Kneeling" at page 253; the unusual key mark at page 256; "LH2E" at page 260; the important reversals of *R* and *L* throughout IV.3, which signify reversal of the whole staging of the exterior of the castle; "Kneeling" at page 267; "Faul go up / Sal xes to LC" at page 268; "XRH" at page 269; "Kneels kisses his hand" at page 270; the stage map at page 273; "2 Pages [follow the King]" at page 280; "Banner Bearer" and the emendation "by compassing your deaths" at page 281.

Someone — probably Kean — has inked a good many fresh cuts (many of which are subsequently marked as "In"). It is not difficult, even in this photographic reproduction, to detect the difference between the original Ellis cuts and the additional Kean cuts. The meticulous Ellis never drew a line through the text without benefit of a ruler, and whenever he cut two or more lines he ruled out the first and last lines of the passage and boxed the cut with ruled vertical lines at each end and through the middle. Wherever in the prompt-book a strike-out is the least bit wavering and "freehand" it be taken to be a Kean cut. Page 200 provides instructive examples. Lines 7 and 8 were *ruled* out by Ellis; lines 1 to 6 were struck out in freehand by Kean or his prompter. In the middle of the same page two lines were roughly *penciled* out by Kean's prompter.

There are many casual pencilings throughout the prompt-book — the sort of quick scribblings that would be made by whoever was holding the book during rehearsal. Some of these come through the photographic process reasonably well and some do not: few are of serious intrinsic importance. One can discern at page 194 a meaningful "taking off hat"; at page 198, "Hubert goes up RH ready to go off"; at page 206 the name of "Keightly" affixed to a trumpet cue; at page 229, "Heralds enter 4 Attend^{s} place chairs on Dais"; at page 239, "Borders down Sc 3"; at page 242, "Re-enter Nobles LH"; at page 250, "Drop Bow and Arrow"; at page 264, "Wings down / Red Mediums 1.2"; at page 281, "Wings down"; and at page 286, "Call Mrs. Kean." There are a great many semilegible penciled notations of the stations and movements of the characters, not worth listing here. The sound cues are numbered in pencil, more or less regularly, from 1 to 39. On the final sheets are penciled notes on specific playing times at the Park and on the arrangement of the scenic units of the fifth act.

MACREADY'S *KING JOHN*

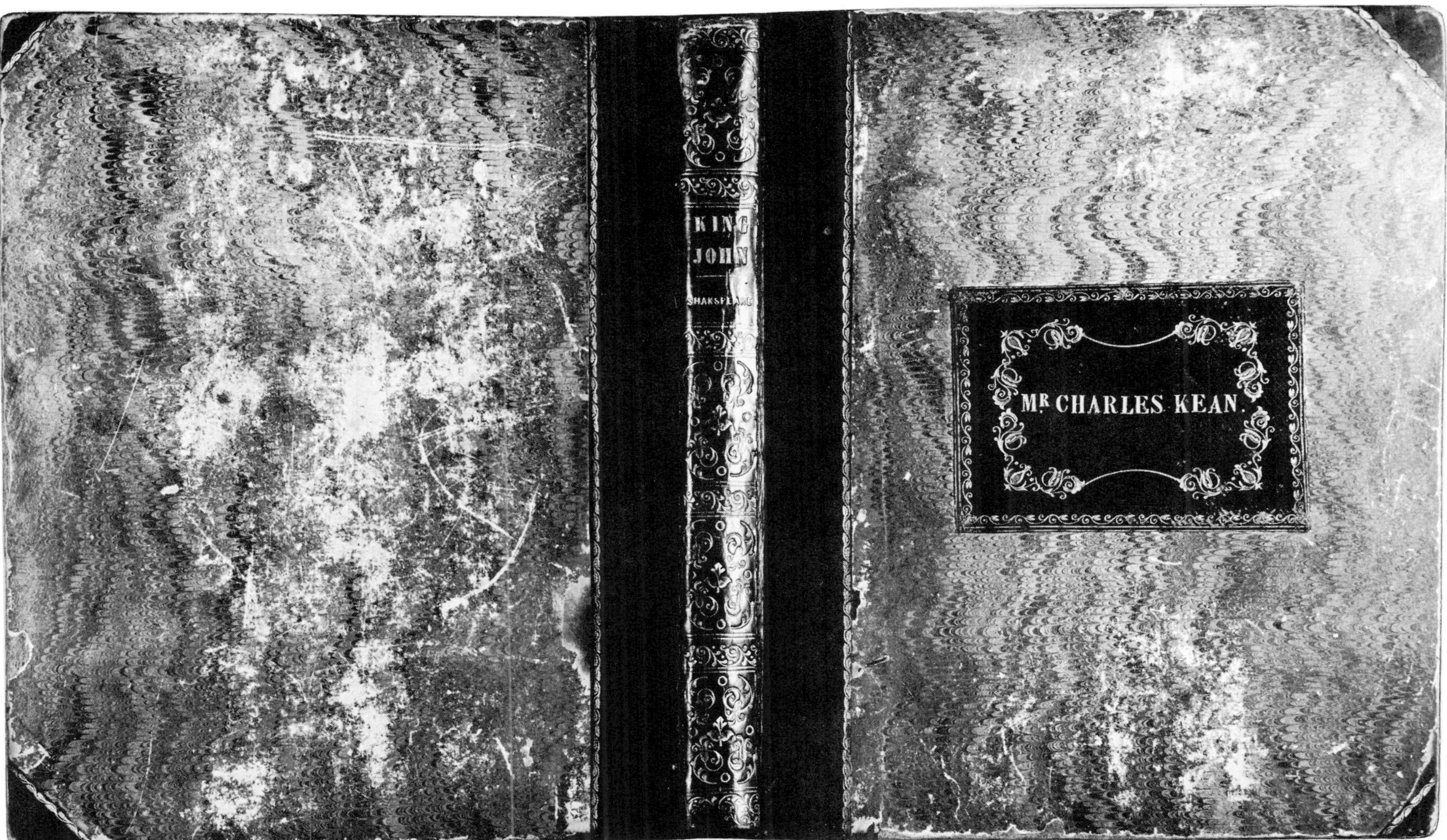
KING
JOHN
SHAKSPEARE
MR CHARLES KEAN.

KING JOHN.*

* King John.] *The troublesome Reign of King John* was written in two parts, by W. Shakspeare and W. Rowley, and printed 1611. But the present play is entirely different, and infinitely superior to it. Pope.

The edition of 1611 has no mention of Rowley, nor in the account of Rowley's works is any mention made of his conjunction with Shakspeare in any play. *King John* was reprinted, in two parts, in 1622. The first edition that I have found of this play, in its present form, is that of 1623, in folio. The edition of 1591 I have not seen. Johnson.

Dr. Johnson mistakes, when he says there is no mention, in Rowley's works, of any conjunction with Shakspeare. *The Birth of Merlin* is ascribed to them jointly, though I cannot believe Shakspeare had any thing to do with it. Mr. Capell is equally mistaken, when he says (Pref. p. 15) that Rowley is called his partner in the title-page of *The Merry Devil of Edmonton.*

There must have been some tradition, however erroneous, upon which Mr. Pope's account was founded. I make no doubt that Rowley wrote the first *King John;* and, when Shakspeare's play was called for, and could not be procured from the players, a piratical bookseller reprinted the old one, with *W. Sh.* in the title-page. Farmer.

The elder play of *King John* was first published in 1591. Shakspeare has preserved the greatest part of the conduct of it, as well as some of the lines. The number of quotations from Horace, and similar scraps of learning scattered over this motley piece, ascertain it to have been the work of a scholar. It contains likewise a quantity of rhyming Latin, and ballad-metre; and in a scene where the Bastard is represented as plundering a monastery, there are strokes of humour, which seem, from their particular turn, to have been most evidently produced by another hand than that of our author.

Of this historical drama there is a subsequent edition in 1611, printed for John Helme, whose name appears before none of the genuine pieces of Shakspeare. I admitted this play some years ago as our author's own, among the twenty which I published from the old editions; but a more careful perusal of it, and a further conviction of his custom of borrowing plots, sentiments, &c. disposes me to recede from that opinion.

Steevens.

A play entitled *The troublesome Raigne of John King of England,* in two parts, was printed in 1591, without the writer's name. It was written, I believe, either by Robert Greene, or George Peele; and certainly preceded this of our author. Mr. Pope, who is very inaccurate in matters of this kind, says that the former was printed in 1611, as written by W. Shakspeare and W. Rowley.

But this is not true. In the *second* edition of this old play, in 1611, the letters *W. Sh.* were put into the title-page, to deceive the purchaser, and to lead him to suppose the piece was Shakspeare's play, which, at that time, was not published. Our author's *King John* was written, I imagine, in 1596. MALONE.

Though this play have the title of *The Life and Death of King John,* yet the action of it begins at the thirty-fourth year of his life, and takes in only some transactions of his reign to the time of his demise, being an interval of about seventeen years.

THEOBALD.

Hall, Holinshed, Stowe, &c. are closely followed, not only in the conduct, but sometimes in the very expressions, throughout the following historical dramas, viz. *Macbeth,* this play, *Richard II. Henry IV.* two parts, *Henry V. Henry VI.* three parts, *Richard III.* and *Henry VIII.*

"A booke called *The Historie of Lord Faulconbridge, bastard Son to Richard Cordelion,*" was entered at Stationers' Hall, Nov. 29, 1614; but I have never met with it, and therefore know not whether it was the old black letter history, or a play upon the same subject. For the original *King John,* see *Six old Plays on which Shakspeare founded,* &c. published by S. Leacroft, Charing-cross.

STEEVENS.

The Historie of Lord Faulconbridge, &c. is a prose narrative, in bl. l. The earliest edition that I have seen of it was printed in 1616.

A book entitled *Richard Cur de Lion* was entered on the Stationers' Books in 1558.

A play called *The Funeral of Richard Cordelion,* was written by Robert Wilson, Henry Chettle, Anthony Mundy, and Michael Drayton, and first exhibited in the year 1598. MALONE.

PERSONS REPRESENTED.

King John:
Prince Henry, *his Son; afterwards King* Henry III.
Arthur, *Duke of* Bretagne, *Son of* Geffrey, *late Duke of* Bretagne, *the elder Brother of King* John.
William Mareshall, *Earl of* Pembroke.
Geffrey Fitz-Peter, *Earl of* Essex, *Chief Justiciary of* England.
William Longsword, *Earl of* Salisbury.[1]
Robert Bigot, *Earl of* Norfolk.
Hubert de Burgh, *Chamberlain to the King.*
Robert Faulconbridge, *Son of Sir* Robert Faulconbridge:
Philip Faulconbridge, *his Half-brother, bastard Son to King* Richard the First.
James Gurney, *Servant to Lady* Faulconbridge.
Peter of Pomfret, *a Prophet.*

Philip, *King of* France.
Lewis, *the Dauphin.*
Archduke of Austria.
Cardinal Pandulph, *the Pope's Legate.*
Melun, *a* French *Lord.*
Chatillon, *Ambassador from* France *to King* John.

Elinor, *the Widow of King* Henry II. *and Mother of King* John.
Constance, *Mother to* Arthur.
Blanch, *Daughter to* Alphonso, *King of* Castile, *and Niece to King* John.
Lady Faulconbridge, *Mother to the Bastard and* Robert Faulconbridge.

Lords, Ladies, Citizens of Angiers, *Sheriff, Heralds, Officers, Soldiers, Messengers, and other Attendants.*

SCENE, sometimes in England, *and sometimes in* France.

1 —— *Salisbury.*] Son to King Henry II. by Rosamond Clifford.

[B Parchment, (large seal on it.) - No 1. —— page 250.
Large Parchment Treaty (several seals on it.) - No 2 —— page 273.
Teller Salisbury

average Time at Park Theatre 1846	
Act. 1st	15
" 2nd	30
" 3rd	38
" 4th	34
" 5th	29
	2" 26
Waits	" 33
	2" 59

Two Hours & Fifty Nine Minutes

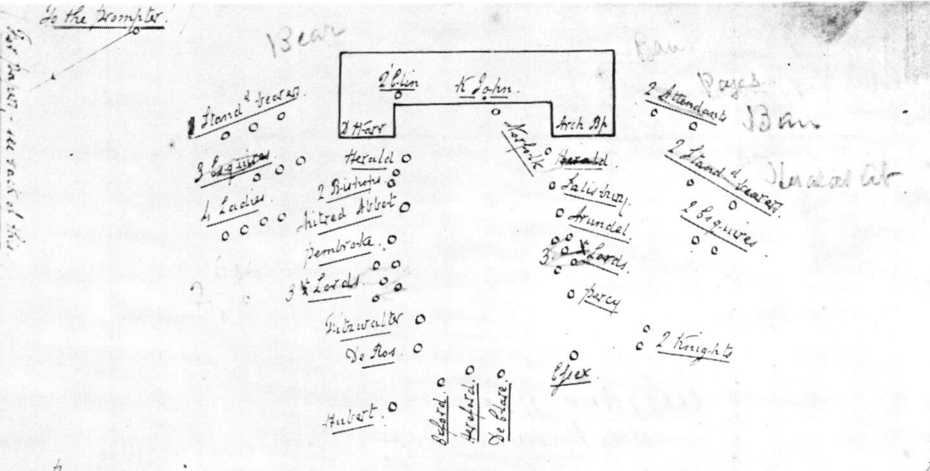

K. John, on Dais, C. seated, - Queen Elinor, seated on a stool, on the King's R. - De Harsenne, (in armour, and bearing the sword of state,) seated on the edge of Dais R. - An Archbishop, seated ditto, L. - Heralds on each side, - The Barons, Bishops, and Knights, form a large circle round the Dais. - Norfolk, (who is disc[d] in the act of speaking to the King, ~~with 2 Knights~~ and Herald (with wand,) - Exit's L. - and returns immed[y], ushering in French Herald, 6 French Barons, and Chatillon - The circle divides, and the attention of all the Characters, is given to the proceedings of the Embassy, who all bow to the King on their entrance.

A loud flourish of trumpets, - kept up till K John ready to speak. ## - L. 1 Ent. in orchestra

R. — K. John. Salisbury. Pembroke. Norfolk. Essex. Hubert. Fitzwalter. De Ros. Oxford. Hereford. De Blare. Percy. Arundel. De Harsenne (State Sword). 2 Knights. 1 & Herald (Wand). 2 Stand[d] Bearers. 4 Esquires. 4 Ladies. 2 Pages.

2 Bishops (Crosiers). Mitred Abbot. 2 Attendants. Archbishop. Q. Elinor. Chatillon. F. Herald (Wand). 6 F. Barons. Sheriff. Philip and Robert Faulconbridge. 2 Drums. 4 Trumpets (for here).

Prompt copy

cut, - marked, - corrected, - &c. &c.
for Charles Kean, Esq.
by - George Ellis (Prompter.)

KING JOHN.

Theatre Royal, Drury Lane
March. - 1846.

ACT I.

SCENE I. ~~Northampton.~~ *A Room of State in the Palace.* (5 Gr.)

~~Enter~~ *King* JOHN, *Queen* ELINOR, PEMBROKE, ESSEX, SALISBURY, *and Others,* ~~*with* CHATILLON.~~ (disc[d].)

Flourish

King John. Now, say, Chatillon, what would France with us?

(L.) *Chat.* Thus, after greeting, speaks the king of France,
In my behaviour,[1] to the majesty,
The borrow'd majesty of England here.

Eli. A strange beginning;—borrow'd majesty!

K. John. Silence, good mother; hear the embassy.

Chat. Philip of France, in right and true behalf
Of thy deceased brother Geffrey's son,
Arthur Plantagenet, lays most lawful claim
To this fair island, and the territories;
To Ireland, Poictiers, Anjou, Touraine, Maine:
Desiring thee to lay aside the sword,
Which sways usurpingly these several titles;
And put the same into young Arthur's hand,
Thy nephew, and right royal sovereign.

[1] *In my behaviour,*] *In my behaviour* means, I think, in the words and action that I am now going to use. MALONE.

K. John. What follows, if we disallow of this?
Chat. The proud control of fierce and bloody war,
To enforce these rights so forcibly withheld.
K. John. Here have we war for war, and blood for blood,
Controlment for controlment: so answer France.
Chat. Then take my king's defiance from my mouth,
The furthest limit of my embassy.
K. John. Bear mine to him, and so depart in peace:
Be thou as lightning in the eyes of France;
For ere thou canst report I will be there,
The thunder of my cannon shall be heard:
So, hence! Be thou the trumpet of our wrath,
And sullen presage of your own decay.—
An honourable conduct let him have:—
Pembroke, look to't: Farewell, Chatillon.
[*Exeunt* CHATILLON ~~and~~ PEMBROKE, &c L.]
Eli. What now, my son? have I not ever said,
How that ambitious Constance would not cease,
Till she had kindled France, and all the world,
Upon the right and party of her son?
This might have been prevented, and made whole,
With very easy arguments of love;
Which now the manage[2] of two kingdoms must
With fearful bloody issue arbitrate.
K. John. Our strong possession, and our right, for us.
Eli. Your strong possession, much more than your right;
Or else it must go wrong with you, and me:
So much my conscience whispers in your ear;
Which none but heaven, and you, and I, shall hear.

[2] — *the manage* —] i. e. conduct, administration.

/Pemb' and 2 Lords, advance & X from R to L, - bowing to the King, - and with ~~Herald~~ and 2 ~~Attendants~~, conduct the Embassy off L. - Queen E. ~~rises, and approaching the King~~, speaks to him, aside, - during which the Court breaks up into small circles, apparently conversing of the King./

/Enter Sheriff of North' - who speaks to Essex./

/All turn to Essex, and continue intent on the business of the Scene./

/The Faulconbridges Enter together, and advancing to C.- both kneel in front of throne./

Nobles &c

Nobles &c

Robt F.

Phil F.

R.- L.-

~~Enter the Sheriff of Northamptonshire, who whispers Essex.~~

Essex. My liege, here is the strangest controversy,
Come from the country to be judg'd by you,
That e'er I heard: Shall I produce the men?
K. John. Let them approach.— [*Exit* Sheriff, L./
Our abbies, and our priories, shall pay

Re-enter Sheriff, *with* ROBERT FAULCONBRIDGE, *and* PHILIP, *his bastard Brother.*] 2. L./

This expedition's charge.—What men are you?
rises |L.| *Bast.* Your faithful subject I, a gentleman,
Born in Northamptonshire; and eldest son,
As I suppose, to Robert Faulconbridge;
A soldier, by the honour-giving hand
Of Cœur-de-lion knighted in the field.
K. John. What art thou?
|R.| *Rob.* The son and heir to that same Faulconbridge.
K. John. Is that the elder, and art thou the heir?
You came not of one mother then, it seems.
Bast. Most certain of one mother, mighty king,
That is well known; and, as I think, one father:
But, for the certain knowledge of that truth,
I put you o'er to heaven, and to my mother;
in ~~Of that I doubt, as all men's children may.~~
Eli. Out on thee, rude man! thou dost shame thy mother,
And wound her honour with this diffidence.
Bast. I, madam? no, I have no reason for it;
That is my brother's plea, and none of mine;
The which if he can prove, 'a pops me out
At least from fair five hundred pound a year:
Heaven guard my mother's honour, and my land!

K. John. A good blunt fellow:—Why, being younger born,
Doth he lay claim to thine inheritance?
Bast. I know not why, except to get the land.
But once he slander'd me with bastardy:
But whe'r[3] I be as true begot, or no,
That still I lay upon my mother's head;
But, that I am as well begot, my liege,
(Fair fall the bones that took the pains for me!)
Compare our faces, and be judge yourself.
If old sir Robert did beget us both,
And were our father, and this son like him;—
O old sir Robert, father, on my knee
I give heaven thanks, I was not like to thee.
K. John. Why, what a madcap hath heaven lent us here!
Eli. He hath a trick of Cœur-de-lion's face,[4]
The accent of his tongue affecteth him:
Do you not read some tokens of my son
In the large composition of this man?
K. John. Mine eye hath well examined his parts,
And finds them perfect Richard.——Sirrah, speak,
What doth move you to claim your brother's land?
Bast. Because he hath a half-face, like my father;
With that half-face[5] would he have all my land:
A half-faced groat five hundred pound a year!

2°

[3] *But* whe'r —] *Whe'r* for *whether*.
[4] *He hath a* trick *of Cœur-de-lion's face,*] By a *trick*, in this place, is meant some peculiarity of look or motion.
[5] *With that* half-face —] The poet sneers at the meagre sharp visage of the elder brother, by comparing him to a silver groat, that bore the king's face in profile, so showed but half the face: the groats of all our Kings of England, and indeed all their other coins of silver, one or two only excepted, had a full face crowned; till Henry VII. at the time above-mentioned, coined groats, and half-groats, as also some shillings, with half-faces, i. e. faces in profile, as all our coin has now.

2°
Lady Faulconbridge
James. Gurney.

ⓧ /slight pause, - Robt F. about to speak, - /

Rob. My gracious liege, when that my father liv'd,
Your brother did employ my father much;—
Bast. Well, sir, by this you cannot get my land:
Your tale must be, how he employ'd my mother.
Rob. And once despatch'd him in an embassy
To Germany, there, with the emperor,
To treat of high affairs touching that time:
The advantage of his absence took the king,
And in the mean time sojourn'd at my father's;
Where how he did prevail, I shame to speak:
But truth is truth; large lengths of seas and shores
Between my father and my mother lay,
(As I have heard my father speak himself,)
When this same lusty gentleman was got.
Upon his death-bed he by will bequeath'd my father did bequeath
His lands to me; and took it, on his death,[6]
That this, my mother's son, was none of his;
And, if he were, he came into the world
Full fourteen weeks before the course of time.
Then, good my liege, let me have what is mine,
My father's land, as was my father's will.
K. John. Sirrah, your brother is legitimate;
Your father's wife did after wedlock bear him:
And, if she did play false, the fault was hers;
Which fault lies on the hazards of all husbands
That marry wives. ⓧ Tell me, how if my brother,
Who, as you say, took pains to get this son,
Had of your father claim'd this son for his?
In sooth, good friend, your father might have kept
This calf, bred from his cow, from all the world;
In sooth, he might: then, if he were my brother's,
My brother might not claim him; nor your father,
Being none of his, refuse him: This concludes,—

[6] —— took it, *on his death,*] i. e. entertained it as his fixed opinion, when he was dying.

~~My mother's son did get your father's heir;~~
Your father's heir must have your father's land.

Rob. Shall then my father's will be of no force,
To dispossess that child which is not his?

Bast. Of no more force to dispossess me, sir,
Than was his will to get me, as I think.

Eli. Whether hadst thou rather,—be a Faulconbridge,
And like thy brother, to enjoy thy land;
Or the reputed son of Cœur-de-lion,
Lord of thy presence, and no land beside?[7]

Bast. Madam, an if my brother had my shape,
And I had his, sir Robert his, like him;[8]
And if my legs were two such riding-rods,
My arms such eel-skins stuff'd; my face so thin,
That in mine ear I durst not stick a rose,
Lest men should say, Look, where three-farthings goes![9]
And, to his shape, were heir to all this land,[1]
'Would I might never stir from off this place,
I'd give it every foot to have this face;
I would not be sir Nob[2] in any case.

[7] *Lord of thy presence, and no land beside?*] *Lord of his presence* apparently signifies, *great in his own person*, and is used in this sense by King John in one of the following scenes.

[8] *And I had his, sir Robert his, like him;*] This is obscure and ill expressed. The meaning is—*If I had his shape, sir Robert's—as he has.*

[9] ——— *my face so thin,*
That in mine ear I durst not stick a rose,
Lest men should say, Look, where three-farthings *goes!*] In this very obscure passage our poet is anticipating the date of another silver coin; humorously to rally a thin face, eclipsed, as it were, by a full blown *rose*. We must observe, to explain this allusion, that Queen Elizabeth was the first, and indeed the only prince, who coined in England three-half-pence, and three farthing pieces.

[1] *And, to his shape, were heir to all this land,*] "*To* his shape," means, in *addition* to the shape he had been just describing.

/rises and descends. – 2nd Elin' follows, and ad's a little towards Philip F. – Some of the Nobles approach the King, as though speaking of the litigants./

Student goes up R H ready to go

Flourish of Trumpets
ready. – R. H. 6.

/Elin' goes up to the King, - while Phil' x'es to Robt R./

/Phil' kneels in front of the King, who strikes him on the R shoulder, with his sword./

Eli. I like thee well; Wilt thou forsake thy fortune,
Bequeath thy land to him, and follow me?
I am a soldier, and now bound to France.
Bast. Brother, take you my land, I'll take my chance:
Your face hath got five hundred pounds a year;
Yet sell your face for five pence, and 'tis dear.—
Madam, I'll follow you unto the death.
Eli. Nay, I would have you go before me thither.
/R/ *Bast.* Our country manners give our betters way.
K. John. What is thy name? /ad^s 1 L.C./
Bast. Philip, my liege; so is my name begun;
Philip, good old sir Robert's wife's eldest son.
K. John. From henceforth bear his name whose form thou bear'st:
Kneel thou down Philip, but arise more great;
Arise sir Richard, and Plantagenet.[3]
Bast. Brother, by the mother's side, give me your hand; /rises./
My father gave me honour, yours gave land:—
Now blessed be the hour, by night or day,
When I was got, sir Robert was away.
~~*Eli.* The very spirit of Plantagenet!~~— /to the King./

[2] *I would not be sir* Nob —] Sir *Nob* is used contemptuously for Sir Robert.

[3] *Arise, sir Richard, and* Plantagenet.] It is a common opinion, that *Plantegenet* was the surname of the royal house of England, from the time of King Henry II. but it is, as Camden observes, in his *Remaines*, 1614, a popular mistake. Plantagenet was not a family name, but a nick-name, by which a grandson of Geffrey, the first Earl of Anjou, was distinguished, from his wearing a *broom-stalk* in his bonnet. But this name was never borne either by the first Earl of Anjou, or by King Henry II. the son of that Earl by the Empress Maude; he being always called Henry *Fitz-Empress;* his son, Richard *Cœur-de-lion*; and the prince who is exhibited in the play before us, John *sans-terre*, or *lack-land*. MALONE.

~~I am thy grandame, Richard; call me so.~~

Bast. Madam, by chance, but not by truth: What though?
Something about, a little from the right,[4]
In at the window, or else o'er the hatch:
Who dares not stir by day, must walk by night;
And have is have, however men do catch:
~~Near or far off, well won is still well shot;~~
And I am I, howe'er I was begot.

K. John. Go, Faulconbridge; now hast thou thy desire,
A landless knight makes thee a landed 'squire.—
Come, madam, and come, Richard; we must speed / to the Court. /
For France, for France; for it is more than need.

~~*Bast.* Brother, adieu; Good fortune come to thee!~~
~~For thou wast got i'the way of honesty.~~ *wert born*

[*Exeunt all but the* Bastard, R-U-E-A-L-/

A foot of honour better than I was;
But many a many foot of land the worse.
Well, now can I make any Joan a lady:——
Good den,[5] *sir Richard,—God-a-mercy, fellow;*—
And if his name be George, I'll call him Peter:
For new-made honour doth forget men's names;
'Tis too respective, and too sociable,

[4] *Something about, a little from the right,* &c.] This speech, composed of allusive and proverbial sentences, is obscure. *I am,* says the sprightly knight, *your grandson,* a little *irregularly,* but every man cannot get what he wishes the legal way. He that *dares not go* about his designs *by day,* must *make his motions* in the *night; he,* to whom the door is shut, must climb the *window,* or leap *the hatch.* This, however, shall not depress me; for the world never enquires how any man got what he is known to possess, but allows that *to have* is *to have,* however it was *caught,* and that he *who wins, shot well,* whatever was his skill, whether the arrow fell *near* the mark, or *far* off it. JOHNSON.

[5] *Good den,*] i. e. a good evening.

Exit Robert R.

Trumpet Flourish, - / R.U.E. /

/ Herald, - De Mar, - Arch-Bp, - and Hubert, precede the King, - who, with Elinor, some of the Nobles, - Pages - Ladies - Bishops, - Ladies, - &c - go off, R.U.E. the others, - with Robt F. Exeunt R. /

BIE Essex.
Arundel - De Roch
Fitz - De Mercy - De Clare
Sheriff
2 Attend.

For your conversion.[6] Now your traveller,—
He and his tooth-pick at my worship's mess;
And when my knightly stomach is suffic'd,
Why then I suck my teeth, and catechise
My picked man of countries:[7]——*My dear sir,*
(Thus, leaning on my elbow, I begin,)
I shall beseech you—That is question now;
And then comes answer like an ABC-book:[8]—
O sir, says answer, *at your best command;*
At your employment; at your service, sir:——
No, sir, says question, *I sweet sir, at yours:*
And so, ere answer knows what question would,
(Saving in dialogue of compliment;
And talking of the Alps and Apennines,
The Pyrenean, and the river Po,)
It draws toward supper in conclusion so.
But this is worshipful society,
And fits the mounting spirit, like myself:
For he is but a bastard to the time,[9]
That doth not smack of observation;
(And so am I, whether I smack, or no;)
And not alone in habit and device,
Exterior form, outward accoutrement;
But from the inward motion to deliver
Sweet, sweet, sweet poison for the age's tooth:
Which, though I will not practise to deceive,
Yet, to avoid deceit, I mean to learn;
For it shall strew the footsteps of my rising.
But who comes in such haste, in riding robes?

6 *'Tis too* respective, *and too sociable,*
For your conversion.] *Respective,* is *respectful, formal.* *Conversion* seems to mean, his late change of condition from a private gentleman to a knight. STEEVENS.

7 *My* picked *man of countries:*] i. e. my *travelled fop.*

8 —— *like an* ABC-book:] An *ABC-book,* or, as they spoke and wrote it, an *absey-book,* is a *catechism.*

9 *For he is but a bastard to the time,* &c.] He is accounted but a mean man in the present age.

What woman-post is this? hath she no husband,
That will take pains to blow a horn before her?

1. 2.

Enter Lady FAULCONBRIDGE, *and* JAMES GURNEY. /L./

O me! it is my mother:—How now, good lady?
What brings you here to court so hastily?
Lady F. Where is that slave, thy brother? where is he?
That holds in chase mine honour up and down?
Bast. My brother Robert? old sir Robert's son?
Colbrand[1] the giant, that same mighty man?
Is it sir Robert's son, that you seek so?
Lady F. Sir Robert's son! Ay, thou unreverend boy,
Sir Robert's son: Why scorn'st thou at sir Robert?
He is sir Robert's son; and so art thou.
Bast. James Gurney, wilt thou give us leave a while? /X'es to him./
Gur. Good leave,[2] good Philip.
Bast. Philip?—sparrow![3]—James,
There's toys abroad;[4] anon I'll tell thee more.
[*Exit* GURNEY. L./

Madam, I was not old sir Robert's son;
Sir Robert might have eat his part in me
Upon Good-friday, and ne'er broke his fast:
Sir Robert could do well; Marry (to confess!)
Could he get me? Sir Robert could not do it;
We know his handy-work:—Therefore, good mother,
To whom am I beholden for these limbs?
Sir Robert never holp to make this leg.

[1] *Colbrand*—] *Colbrand* was a Danish giant, whom Guy of Warwick discomfited in the presence of King Athelstan.
[2] *Good leave,* &c.] *Good leave* means a *ready assent.*
[3] *Philip?—sparrow!*] A sparrow is called Philip.
[4] *There's toys abroad;* &c.] i. e. rumours idle reports.

⊗ /advancing to him./

|R.| *Lady F.* Hast thou conspired with thy brother too,
That for thine own gain should'st defend mine honour?
What means this scorn, thou most untoward knave? ⊗

|L.| *Bast.* Knight, knight, good mother,—Basilisco-like:[5]
What! I am dubb'd; I have it on my shoulder.
But, mother, I am not sir Robert's son;
I have disclaim'd sir Robert, and my land;
Legitimation, name, and all is gone:
Then, good my mother, let me know my father;
Some proper man, I hope; Who was it, mother?

Lady F. Hast thou denied thyself a Faulconbridge?

Bast. As faithfully as I deny the devil.

Lady F. King Richard Cœur-de-lion was thy father;
By long and vehement suit I was seduc'd
To make room for him in my husband's bed:—
Heaven lay not my transgression to my charge!—
Thou art the issue of my dear offence,
Which was so strongly urg'd, past my defence.

Bast. Now, by this light, were't I to get again,
Madam, I would not wish a better father.
Some sins do bear their privilege on earth,
And so doth yours; your fault was not your folly:
Needs must you lay your heart at his dispose,—
Subjected tribute to commanding love,—
Against whose fury and unmatched force
The awless lion could not wage the fight,
Nor keep his princely heart from Richard's hand.

[5] Knight, knight, *good mother,—Basilisco-like:*] Faulconbridge's words here carry a concealed piece of satire on a stupid drama of that age, printed in 1599, and called *Soliman and Perseda.* In this piece there is a character of a bragging cowardly knight, called Basilisco.

He, that perforce robs lions of their hearts,
May easily win a woman's. Ay, my mother,
With all my heart I thank thee for my father!
Who lives and dares but say, thou did'st not well
When I was got, I'll send his soul to hell.
Come, lady, I will show thee to my kin;
And they shall say, when Richard me begot,
If thou hadst said him nay, it had been sin:
Who says it was, he lies; I say, 'twas not.

[*Exeunt*.

ACT II.

SCENE I. France. *Before the Walls of* Angiers.

Enter, on one side, the Archduke of Austria, *and Forces; on the other,* PHILIP, *King of* France, *and Forces;* LEWIS, CONSTANCE, ARTHUR, *and Attendants.*

Lew. Before Angiers well met, brave Austria.—
Arthur, that great fore-runner of thy blood,
Richard, that robb'd the lion of his heart,
And fought the holy wars in Palestine,
By this brave duke came early to his grave:
And, for amends to his posterity,
At our importance[6] hither is he come,
To spread his colours, boy, in thy behalf;
And to rebuke the usurpation
Of thy unnatural uncle, English John:
Embrace him, love him, give him welcome hither.

Arth. God shall forgive you Cœur-de-lion's death,

[6] *At our* importance —] At our *importunity*.

King.

Trumpets. R

Sentinels are disc[d] on the walls of Angiers, L. - A Herald, and several French Nobles, precede K Philip, &c R. - Constance - Arthur - and their Attendants, follow. - Austria's Knights and Banner, precede him L. - Standards are borne before the French King, - Banner of England, before Arthur; - K Phil. adv's to meet Aust.

All in Act I. - change!

Time. - 15 Min's.

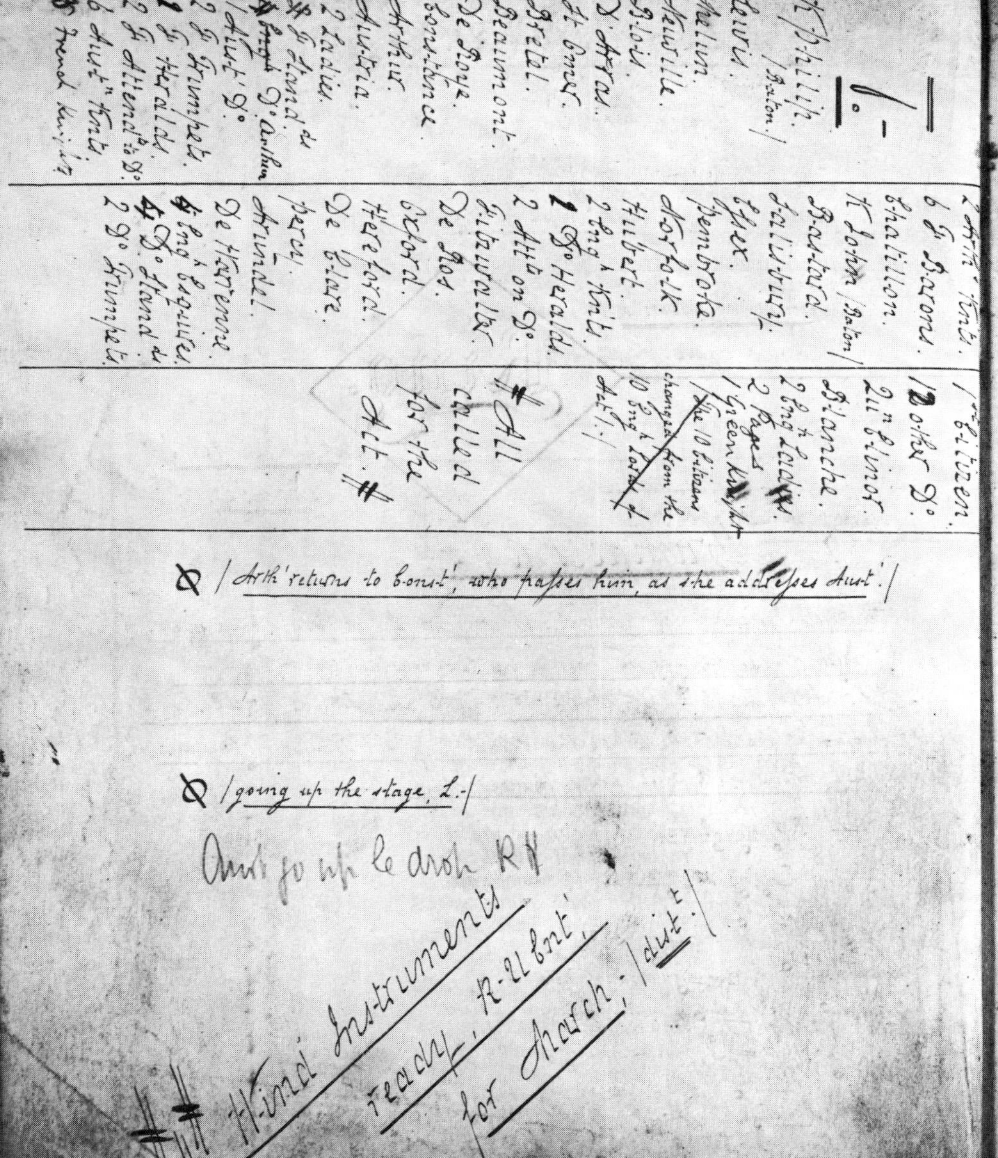

The rather, that you give his offspring life,
Shadowing their right under your wings of war:
I give you welcome with a powerless hand,
But with a heart full of unstained love:
Welcome before the gates of Angiers, duke.

Lew. A noble boy! Who would not do thee right?

Aust. Upon thy cheek lay I this zealous kiss,
As seal to this indenture of my love;
That to my home I will no more return,
Till Angiers, and the right thou hast in France,
Together with that pale, that white-fac'd shore,
Whose foot spurns back the ocean's roaring tides,
And coops from other lands her islanders,
Even till that England, hedg'd in with the main,
That water-walled bulwark, still secure
And confident from foreign purposes,
Even till that utmost corner of the west
Salute thee for her king: till then, fair boy,
Will I not think of home, but follow arms.

Const. O, take his mother's thanks, a widow's thanks,
Till your strong hand shall help to give him strength,
To make a more requital to your love.

Aust. The peace of heaven is theirs, that lift their swords
In such a just and charitable war.

K. Phi. Well then, to work; our cannon shall be bent
Against the brows of this resisting town.——
~~Call for our chiefest men of discipline,~~
~~To cull the plots of best advantages:~~[7]—
We'll lay before this town our royal bones,

[7] *To cull the plots of best advantages:*] i. e. to mark such stations as might over-awe the town.

~~Wade to the market-place in Frenchmen's blood,~~
But we will make it subject to this boy.
Const. Stay for an answer to your embassy,
Cut –[Lest unadvis'd you stain your swords with blood:
My lord Chatillon may from England bring
That right in peace, which here we urge in war;
And then we shall repent each drop of blood,
That hot rash haste so indirectly shed.

Enter CHATILLON, and Suite, – (R. U. E.)

K. Phi. A wonder, lady!—lo, upon thy wish,
Our messenger Chatillon is arriv'd.—
What England says, say briefly, gentle lord,
~~We coldly pause for thee; Chatillon, speak.~~
Chat. Then turn your forces from this paltry siege,
And stir them up against a mightier task.
England, impatient of your just demands,
Hath put himself in arms; the adverse winds,
Whose leisure I have staid, have given him time
To land his legions all as soon as I:
His marches are expedient[8] to this town,
His forces strong, his soldiers confident.
With him along is come the mother-queen,
An Até, stirring him to blood and strife;
With her her niece, the lady Blanch of Spain;
With them a bastard of the king deceas'd:
And all the unsettled humours of the land,—
~~Rash, inconsiderate, fiery voluntaries,~~
With ladies' faces, and fierce dragons' spleens,—
Have sold their fortunes at their native homes,
Bearing their birthrights proudly on their backs,
~~To make a hazard of new fortunes here.~~
In brief, a braver choice of dauntless spirits,
Than now the English bottoms have waft o'er,

[8] —— *expedient* —] Immediate, *expeditious.*

(Aust.' goes up R. B., as reconnoitring, and comes down R. corner.)

4 Knights
Trumpet, – R. U. E. – (All turn to the sound, – Chatillon and 6 Fr. Barons, enter, up stage, as from the plain below, and remain at the back, near R. U. E.)

6 French Barons
Chat.
K. Phil.
R. L.

5 Distant March, – R. U. E. –
(Movement of all on the Stage, – looking out, R. U. E.)

Change places a few.
Dauph. go up look off

March - forte !

/ Phil X'es to the Dauph - that & party go down to back of Const. /

/ With Essex, - Hubert - Salisbury, - Norfolk - Fitzwalter - Oxford, Percy, - De Ros, - Arundel, - De Warrenne, - Hereford, - the Bastard, - K John, - 2 Elinor, - Blanch, - 2 Eng' Knights, - 2 Eng' Heralds - 5 Eng' Esquires, - 5 Eng' Standards, - 2 Attend^ts on Heralds - 2 Trumpets, - 2 Ladies / Queen's Attend^ts / - &c. - All Enter, up R.U.E. - and occupy the L - side of stage. /

5 Standards.
5 Esquires
2 Knights
2 Trumpets.
2 Heralds
2 Attend^ts
Pembroke.
De Warr.
Hereford.
K John.
Norfolk
2 Pages
De Ros.
Queen E
2 Ladies
De Clare
Blanch
Salisbury
Arundel.
Percy.
Green Knight
Bastard
Oxford
Fitzwalter
Aust^n Stand^d
Aust Knights
Line
Hubert.
Essex.

R. - L.

Did never float upon the swelling tide,
To do offence and scath[9] in Christendom.
The interruption of their churlish drums
[Drums beat.
Cuts off more circumstance: they are at hand,
To parley, or to fight; therefore, prepare.

K. Phi. How much unlook'd for is this expedition!

Aust. By how much unexpected, by so much
We must awake endeavour for defence;
For courage mounteth with occasion:
Let them be welcome then, we are prepar'd

/ R.U.E. /

Enter King JOHN, ELINOR, BLANCH, *the* Bastard, PEMBROKE, *and Forces*,

K. John. Peace be to France; if France in peace permit
Our just and lineal entrance to our own!
If not, bleed France, and peace ascend to heaven!
Whiles we, God's wrathful agent, do correct
Their proud contempt that beat his peace to heaven.

K. Phi. Peace be to England; if that war return
From France to England, there to live in peace!
England we love; and, for that England's sake,
With burden of our armour here we sweat:
This toil of ours should be a work of thine;
But thou from loving England art so far,
That thou hast under-wrought[1] his lawful king,
Cut off the sequence of posterity,
Outfaced infant state, and done a rape
Upon the maiden virtue of the crown.
Look here upon thy brother Geffrey's face ;—
/ taking Arthur in his R H, - on R. /

[9] — *scath* —] Destruction, harm.
[1] — *under-wrought* —] i. e. underworked, undermined.

These eyes, these brows, were moulded out of his:
This little abstract doth contain that large,
Which died in Geffrey; and the hand of time
Shall draw this brief[2] into as huge a volume.
That Geffrey was thy elder brother born,
And this his son; England was Geffrey's right,
And this is Geffrey's: In the name of God,
How comes it then, that thou art call'd a king,
When living blood doth in these temples beat,
Which owe the crown that thou o'er-masterest?

K. John. From whom hast thou this great commission, France,
To draw my answer from thy articles?

K. Phi. From that supernal judge, that stirs good thoughts
In any breast of strong authority,
To look into the blots and stains of right.
That judge hath made me guardian to this boy:
Under whose warrant, I impeach thy wrong;
And, by whose help, I mean to chastise it.

K. John. Alack, thou dost usurp authority.

K. Phi. Excuse; it is to beat usurping down.

Eli. Who is it, thou dost call usurper, France?

Const. Let me make answer;—thy usurping son.

Eli. Out, insolent! thy bastard shall be king;
That thou may'st be a queen, and check the world!

Const. My bed was ever to thy son as true,
As thine was to thy husband: and this boy
Liker in feature to his father Geffrey,
Than thou and John in manners; being as like,
As rain to water, or devil to his dam.
My boy a bastard! By my soul, I think,

[2] —— *this* brief —] A *brief* is a short writing, abstract, or description.

His father never was so true begot;
It cannot be, an if thou wert his mother.[3]

Eli. There's a good mother, boy, that blots thy father.

Const. There's a good grandam, boy, that would blot thee.

Aust. Peace!

Bast. Hear the crier.

Aust. What the devil art thou?

Bast. One that will play the devil, sir, with you,
An 'a may catch your hide and you alone.[4]
You are the hare of whom the proverb goes,
Whose valour plucks dead lions by the beard;
I'll smoke your skin-coat, an I catch you right;
Sirrah, look to't; i'faith, I will, i'faith.

Blanch. O, well did he become that lion's robe,
That did disrobe the lion of that robe!

Bast. It lies as sightly on the back of him,
As great Alcides' shoes upon an ass:—
But, ass, I'll take that burden from your back;
Or lay on that, shall make your shoulders crack.

Aust. What cracker is this same, that deafs our ears
With this abundance of superfluous breath?

K. Phi. Lewis, determine what we shall do straight.

[3] —— *an if* thou *wert his mother.*] Constance alludes to Elinor's infidelity to her husband, Lewis the Seventh, when they were in the Holy Land; on account of which he was divorced from her. She afterwards (1151) married our King Henry II.

[4] *One that will play the devil, sir, with you,*
An 'a may catch your hide *and you alone.*] The story is, that Austria, who killed King Richard *Cœur-de-lion*, wore, as the spoil of that prince, a lion's *hide*, which had belonged to him.

Lew. Women and fools, break off your conference.— /goes up to E./
King John, this is the very sum of all,—
England, and Ireland, Anjou, Touraine, Maine,
In right of Arthur do I claim of thee:
Wilt thou resign them, and lay down thy arms?
K. John. My life as soon:—I do defy thee, France.
Arthur of Bretagne, yield thee to my hand;
And, out of my dear love, I'll give thee more
Than e'er the coward hand of France can win:
Submit thee, boy.
Eli. Come to thy grandam, child.
Const. Do, child, go to it' grandam, child;
Give grandam kingdom, and it' grandam will
Give it a plum, a cherry, and a fig:
There's a good grandam.
Arth. Good my mother, peace!
I would, that I were low laid in my grave;
I am not worth this coil that's made for me.
Eli. His mother shames him so, poor boy, he weeps.
Const. Now shame upon you, whe'r she does, or no!
His grandam's wrongs, and not his mother's shames,
Draw those heaven-moving pearls from his poor eyes,
Which heaven shall take in nature of a fee;
Ay, with these crystal beads heaven shall be brib'd
To do him justice, and revenge on you.
Eli. Thou monstrous slanderer of heaven and earth!
Const. Thou monstrous injurer of heaven and earth!
Call not me slanderer; thou, and thine, usurp
The dominations, royalties, and rights,
Of this oppressed boy: This is thy eldest son's son,
Infortunate in nothing but in thee;

/Arth' quits K. Phil', and goes back, alarmed, to his mother's side./

Trumpets ready. 1:

Thy sins are visited in this poor child;
The cannon of the law is laid on him,
Being but the second generation
Removed from thy sin-conceiving womb.

K. John. Bedlam, have done.

Const. I have but this to say,—
That he's not only plagued for her sin,
But God hath made her sin and her the plague[5]
On this removed issue, plagu'd for her,
And with her plague, her sin; his injury
Her injury,—the beadle to her sin;
All punish'd in the person of this child,
And all for her; A plague upon her!

Eli. Thou unadvised scold, I can produce
A will, that bars the title of thy son.

Const. Ay, who doubts that? a will! a wicked will;
A woman's will; a canker'd grandam's will!

[5] *I have but this to say,—*
That he's not only plagued for her sin,
But God hath made her sin and her the plague, &c.] The Commentators have laboured hard to make out a meaning in this passage. The following by Mr. Henley seems as satisfactory as any. Young Arthur is here represented as not only suffering *from* the guilt of his grandmother; but, also, by *her*, in person, she being made the very instrument of his sufferings. As he was not her *immediate*, but REMOVED *issue*—the *second generation from her sin-conceiving womb*—it might have been expected, that the evils to which, upon her account, he was obnoxious, would have *incidentally* befallen him; instead of his being punished for them all, by *her* immediate *infliction.*—He is not only plagued on account of her sin, according to the threatening of the commandment, but she is preserved alive to her *second generation,* to be the instrument of inflicting on her grandchild the penalty annexed to her sin; so that *he is plagued on her account*, and *with her plague*, which is, *her sin*, that is [taking, by a common figure, the cause for the consequence] the *penalty entailed upon it*. HIS *injury*, or *the evil* he *suffers*, her *sin brings upon him*, and HER *injury*, or, *the evil* she *inflicts, he suffers from* her, as *the beadle to her sin*, or *executioner of the punishment annexed to it*.

K. Phi. Peace, lady; pause, or be more temperate:
It ill beseems this presence, to cry aim[6]
To these ill-tuned repetitions.—
Some trumpet summon hither to the walls
These men of Angiers; let us hear them speak,
Whose title they admit, Arthur's or John's.

Trumpets sound. Enter Citizens *upon the walls.*

1 *Cit.* Who is it, that hath warn'd us to the walls?
K. Phi. 'Tis France, for England.
K. John. England, for itself:
You men of Angiers, and my loving subjects,—
K. Phi. You loving men of Angiers, Arthur's subjects,
Our trumpet call'd you to this gentle parle.
K. John. For our advantage;—Therefore, hear us first.——
These flags of France, that are advanced here
Before the eye and prospect of your town,
Have hither march'd to your endamagement:
The cannons have their bowels full of wrath;
And ready mounted are they, to spit forth
Their iron indignation 'gainst your walls:
All preparation for a bloody siege,
And merciless proceeding by these French,
Confront your city's eyes, your winking gates;[7]
And, but for our approach, those sleeping stones,
That as a waist do girdle you about,
By the compulsion of their ordnance
By this time from their fixed beds of lime

[6] *It ill beseems this presence, to cry* aim—] To *cry aim* is borrowed probably from archery, and means to incite notice, or raise attention.

[7] —— *your* winking *gates;*] i. e. gates hastily closed from an apprehension of danger.

/ Fr. Herald, and Trumpet, advance to C. - and sound, - / at end of K. P.'s speech. / - ~~By K. John's direction, Eng. Herald, and Trumpet, do the same.~~ - All turn towards the walls. - After a pause, -

Trumpets answer, from within, L. -

as tho' a little way off. - 1st Citizen, with 4 others, - in arms, - appear upon the walls, in front L. - All are intent upon the speakers, thro' the Scene. /

/ Overbearing each appeal of K. Philip's. /

Had been dishabited, and wide havock made
For bloody power to rush upon your peace.
But, on the sight of us, your lawful king,—
Who painfully, with much expedient march,
Have brought a countercheck before your gates,
To save unscratch'd your city's threaten'd cheeks,—
Behold, the French, amaz'd, vouchsafe a parle:
And now, instead of bullets wrapp'd in fire,
To make a shaking fever in your walls,
They shoot but calm words, folded up in smoke,
To make a faithless error in your ears:
Which trust accordingly, kind citizens,
And let us in, your king; whose labour'd spirits,
Forwearied[8] in this action of swift speed,
Crave harbourage within your city walls.

K. Phi. When I have said, make answer to us both.
Lo, in this right hand, whose protection
Is most divinely vow'd upon the right
Of him it holds, stands young Plantagenet;
Son to the elder brother of this man,
And king o'er him, and all that he enjoys:
For this down-trodden equity, we tread
In warlike march these greens before your town;
Being no further enemy to you,
Than the constraint of hospitable zeal,
In the relief of this oppressed child,
Religiously provokes. Be pleased then
To pay that duty, which you truly owe,
To him that owes it;[9] namely, this young prince:
And then our arms, like to a muzzled bear,
Save in aspéct, have all offence seal'd up;
Our cannons' malice vainly shall be spent
Against the invulnerable clouds of heaven;

[8] *Forwearied*—] i. e. worn out, Sax.
[9] *To him that* owes *it;*] i. e. *owns* it.

[taking Arthur, up a little, R.C.]

Ready for Shouts;—
Trumpet Alarums;—
and to work Brashes,
Braces & Chains; &c;—
R.U.E.,— at back.

And, with a blessed and unvex'd retire,
With unhack'd swords, and helmets all unbruis'd,
We will bear home that lusty blood again,
Which here we came to spout against your town,
And leave your children, wives, and you, in peace.
But if you fondly pass our proffer'd offer,
'Tis not the roundure[1] of your old-fac'd walls
Can hide you from our messengers of war;
Though all these English, and their discipline,
Were harbour'd in their rude circumference.
Then, tell us, shall your city call us lord,
In that behalf which we have challeng'd it?
Or shall we give the signal to our rage,
And stalk in blood to our possession?

1 *Cit.* In brief, we are the king of England's subjects;
For him, and in his right, we hold this town.

K. John. Acknowledge then the king, and let me in.

1 *Cit.* That can we not: but he that proves the king,
To him will we prove loyal; till that time,
Have we ramm'd up our gates against the world.

K. John. Doth not the crown of England prove the king?
And, if not that, I bring you witnesses,
Twice fifteen thousand hearts of England's breed,—

Bast. Bastards, and else.

K. John. To verify our title with their lives.

K. Phi. As many, and as well-born bloods as those,——

Bast. Some bastards too.

K. Phi. Stand in his face, to contradict his claim.

1 *Cit.* Till you compound whose right is worthiest,
We, for the worthiest, hold the right from both.

[1] *'Tis not the* roundure, *&c.*] *Roundure*, means the same as the French *rondure*, i. e. the circle.

Wind.

Noise of Battle &c.

⌽ /goes down, L. - a general movement of all on the stage, as preparing for the contest./

Flourish 8

K John. - Up higher to the plain! - where we'll set forth
In best appointment, all our regiments
Bast. - Speed, then, to take advantage of the field!
K Phil. - /to Lewis./ - It shall be so, - and, at the other hill
Command the rest to stand, - God, and our right! /Exit 2 E. R./
Bast. - St George, - that swing'd &c

/During the above three speeches, all the French party, exeunt 1st & 2nd Ent. R. - and the English, - R. U. E. - Lewis stops K Phil. and speaks with him, and Austria, as if on the ensuing battle. - Aust. then X's to L. - with a French Knight, as tho' giving him directions. - The Bastard waits to take his shield, from his Esquire, and is employed with him in bracing it on, when, as the Arch-Duke X's back again from L to R. Faulc. going R. U. E. - calls out to him, - "Sirrah, were I at home &c /

⊘ /The Trumpeters sound before the Herald speaks./

K. John. Then ~~God~~ heaven forgive the sin of all those souls, ⌽
That to their everlasting residence,
Before the dew of evening fall, shall fleet,
In dreadful trial of our kingdom's king!

K. Phi. Amen, Amen!—Mount, chevaliers! to arms!

Bast. St. George,—that swing'd the dragon, and e'er since,
Sits on his horseback at mine hostess' door,
Teach us some fence!—Sirrah, were I at home,
At your den, sirrah, [*To* Austria] with your lioness,
I'd set an ox-head to your lion's hide,
And make a monster of you.

Aust. Peace; no more. /Exit R./

Bast. O, tremble; for you hear the lion roar. /Exit R. U. E./

~~*K. John.* Up higher to the plain; where we'll set forth,~~
~~In best appointment, all our regiments.~~
~~*Bast.* Speed then, to take advantage of the field.~~
~~*K. Phi.* It shall be so;—[*To* Lewis] and at the other hill~~
~~Command the rest to stand.—God, and our right!~~
~~[*Exeunt.*~~

~~SCENE II.~~

~~*The same.*~~

/R. 2 E./

Alarums ~~*and Excursions; then a Retreat.*~~ *Enter a French* Herald, [*with trumpets, and 2 Attendants.*] *to the gates.* ⊘

F. Her. You men of Angiers, open wide your gates,
And let young Arthur, duke of Bretagne, in;
Who, by the hand of France, this day hath made
Much work for tears in many an English mother,

Shouts. — Flourish. — Trumpet Alarum

/This is done 3 distinct times!!! - commencing each time very loud and concluding very remote./

/The Citizens seem to watch the Battle, from the walls./

Whose sons lye scatter'd on the bleeding ground:
Many a widow's husband groveling lies,
Coldly embracing the discolour'd earth;
And victory, with little loss, doth play
Upon the dancing banners of the French;
Who are at hand, triumphantly display'd,
To enter conquerors, and to proclaim
Arthur of Bretagne, England's king, and yours.

Enter an English Herald, *with* 2 *trumpets,* and 2 Attendants. - R.U.E. - The English Trumpets sound.

E. Her. Rejoice, you men of Angiers, ring your bells;
King John, your king and England's, doth approach,
Commander of this hot malicious day!
Their armours, that march'd hence so silver-bright,
Hither return all gilt with Frenchmen's blood;
There stuck no plume in any English crest,
That is removed by a staff of France;
Our colours do return in those same hands
That did display them when we first march'd forth;
And, like a jolly troop of huntsmen, come
Our lusty English, all with purpled hands,
Died in the dying slaughter of their foes:
Open your gates, and give the victors way

Cit. Heralds, from off our towers we might behold,
From first to last, the onset and retire
Of both your armies; whose equality
By our best eyes cannot be censured:[2]
Blood hath bought blood, and blows have answer'd blows;
Strength match'd with strength, and power confronted power:

[2] —— *cannot be* censured:] i. e. cannot be estimated. Our author ought rather to have written—whose *superiority*, or whose *inequality*, cannot be censured.

Flourish on the Stage ready. - R.U.E.

Loud Flourish of Trumpets, on the Stage

Each party occupy their previous positions, - the English Enter, a little in advance of the French, - both parties with their eyes and hands directed to the Citizens on the walls, as if expecting to enter, - very rapid entrance, - When John speaks, all turn to him, - the Austrian party who were on the L, - now enter mingled with the French party.

Both are alike; and both alike we like.
One must prove greatest: while they weigh so even,
We hold our town for neither; yet for both.

Enter, at ~~one side~~ R.U.E. King JOHN, *with his power;* ELINOR, BLANCH, *and the* Bastard; *at the ~~other~~* 2 L.R.- *King* PHILIP, LEWIS, AUSTRIA, *and Forces.*

/up L./ *K. John.* France, hast thou yet more blood to cast away?
Say, shall the current of our right run on?
Whose passage, vex'd with thy impediment,
Shall leave his native channel, and o'er-swell
With course disturb'd even thy confining shores;
Unless thou let his silver water keep
A peaceful progress to the ocean.

/up R./ *K. Phi.* England, thou hast not sav'd one drop of blood,
In this hot trial, more than we of France;
Rather, lost more: And by this hand I swear,
That sways the earth this climate overlooks,—
Before we will lay down our just-borne arms,
We'll put thee down, 'gainst whom these arms we bear,
Or add a royal number to the dead;
Gracing the scroll, that tells of this war's loss,
With slaughter coupled to the name of kings.

Bast. Ha, majesty! how high thy glory towers, /in front L.L./
When the rich blood of kings is set on fire!
O, now doth death line his dead chaps with steel;
The swords of soldiers are his teeth, his fangs;
And now he feasts, mouthing the flesh of men,
In undetermin'd differences of kings.—
Why stand these royal fronts amazed thus?
Cry, havock, kings! back to the stained field,
You equal potents,[8] fiery-kindled spirits!

[8] *You equal potents,*] *Potents* for potentates.

Then let confusion of one part confirm
The other's peace; till then, blows, blood, and death!

K. John. Whose party do the townsmen yet admit? Φ

K. Phi. Speak, citizens, for England; who's your king?

1 *Cit.* The king of England, when we know the king.

K. Phi. Know him in us, that here hold up his right.

K. John. In us, that are our own great deputy,
And bear possession of our person here;
Lord of our presence, Angiers, and of you.

1 *Cit.* A greater power than we, denies all this;
And, till it be undoubted, we do lock
Our former scruple in our strong-barr'd gates:
King'd of our fears;[4] until our fears, resolv'd,
Be by some certain king purg'd and depos'd.

Bast. By heaven, these scroyles of Angiers[5] flout you, kings;
And stand securely on their battlements,
As in a theatre, whence they gape and point
At your industrious scenes and acts of death.
Your royal presences be rul'd by me; Φ
Do like the mutines of Jerusalem,[6]
Be friends a while, and both conjointly bend
Your sharpest deeds of malice on this town:
By east and west let France and England mount
Their battering cannon, charged to the mouths;
Till their soul-fearing clamours[7] have brawl'd down

[4] *King'd of our fears;*] i. e. ruled by our fears.

[5] —— *these* scroyles *of Angiers*—] *Escroulles,* Fr. i. e. scabby, scrophulous fellows.

[6] *Do like the* mutines *of Jerusalem,*] The *mutines* are the *mutineers,* the seditious.

[7] *Till their* soul-fearing *clamours*—] i. e. soul-appalling.

Φ / All turn their eyes to the walls. /

Φ / X'es to L.– K John comes down L. /

Φ /The Citizens earnestly consult together./

Ø /The Bastard goes down L,- as K. John X'es to K. Phil./

Φ /The combatants press forward, looking to the Kings for the word or signal, to set on. - The Kings in conference./

The flinty ribs of this contemptuous city: Φ
I'd play incessantly upon these jades,
Even till unfenced desolation
Leave them as naked as the vulgar air.
That done, dissever your united strengths,
And part your mingled colours once again;
Turn face to face, and bloody point to point:
Then, in a moment, fortune shall cull forth
Out of one side her happy minion;
To whom in favour she shall give the day,
And kiss him with a glorious victory. X L.H.
How like you this wild counsel, mighty states?
Smacks it not something of the policy?

Ø *K. John.* Now, by the sky that hangs above our heads, /X'es L./
I like it well;—France, shall we knit our powers,
And lay this Angiers even with the ground;
Then, after, fight who shall be king of it?

Bast. An if thou hast the mettle of a king,—
Being wrong'd, as we are by this peevish town,—
Turn thou the mouth of thy artillery,
As we will ours, against these saucy walls:
And when that we have dash'd them to the ground,
Why, then defy each other; and, pell-mell,
Make work upon ourselves, for heaven, or hell.

K. Phi. Let it be so:—Say, where will you assault?

Φ *K. John.* We from the west will send destruction
Into this city's bosom.

Aust. I from the north.

K. Phi. Our thunder from the south,
Shall rain their drift of bullets on this town.

Bast. O prudent discipline! From north to south;
Austria and France shoot in each other's mouth: [*Aside.*

I'll stir them to it:—Come, away, away!

1 *Cit.* Hear us, great kings: vouchsafe a while to stay,
And I shall show you peace, and fair-faced league;
Win you this city without stroke, or wound;
Rescue those breathing lives to die in beds,
That here come sacrifices for the field:
Persévere not, but hear me, mighty kings.

K. John. Speak on, with favour; we are bent to hear.

1 *Cit.* That daughter there of Spain, the lady Blanch,[8]
Is near to England; Look upon the years
Of Lewis the Dauphin, and that lovely maid:
If lusty love should go in quest of beauty,
Where should he find it fairer than in Blanch?
If zealous love should go in search of virtue,
Where should he find it purer than in Blanch?
If love ambitious sought a match of birth,
Whose veins bound richer blood than lady Blanch?
Such as she is, in beauty, virtue, birth,
Is the young Dauphin every way complete:
If not complete, O say, he is not she;
And she again wants nothing, to name want,
If want it be not, that she is not he:
He is the half part of a blessed man,
Left to be finished by such a she;
And she a fair divided excellence,
Whose fulness of perfection lies in him.
O, two such silver currents, when they join,
Do glorify the banks that bound them in:
And two such shores to two such streams made one,
Two such controlling bounds shall you be, kings,
To these two princes, if you marry them.

[8] —— *the lady* Blanch,] The lady *Blanch* was daughter to Alphonso the Ninth, King of Castile, and was niece to King John by his sister Elianor.

/ Going up C, – hurrying them away, – the French, R, – the English, R.U.E, – Austrian, L. – All stop, and turn to the Citizen when he speaks. /

/ All raise their swords, and are going away. /

/ The Nobles, &c, have broke into various groups, by the end of this speech, and appear to be remarking on the proposal, and its effect on the Kings, – Elinor is urgently speaking to K John, – Lewis & Philip, in debate, on R, – are joined by Austria. /

Thy now unsur'd assurance to the crown.
I see a yielding - &c -

This union shall do more than battery can,
To our fast-closed gates; for, at this match,
With swifter spleen[9] than powder can enforce,
The mouth of passage shall we fling them wide ope,
And give you entrance; but, without this match,
The sea enraged is not half so deaf,
Lions more confident, mountains and rocks
More free from motion; no, not death himself
In mortal fury half so peremptory,
As we to keep this city.

Bast. Here's a stay,[1]
That shakes the rotten carcase of old death
Out of his rags! Here's a large mouth, indeed,
That spits forth death, and mountains, rocks, and seas;
Talks as familiarly of roaring lions,
As maids of thirteen do of puppy-dogs!
What cannoneer begot this lusty blood?
He speaks plain cannon, fire, and smoke, and bounce;
He gives the bastinado with his tongue;
Our ears are cudgel'd; not a word of his,
But buffets better than a fist of France:
Zounds! I was never so bethump'd with words,
Since I first call'd my brother's father, dad.

Eli. Son, list to this conjunction, make this match;
Give with our niece a dowry large enough:
For by this knot thou shalt still surely tie
Thy now unsur'd assurance to the crown,
That yon green boy shall have no sun to ripe
The bloom that promiseth a mighty fruit.

[9] —— *at this match,*
With swifter spleen, &c.] Our author uses *spleen* for any violent hurry, or tumultuous speed.

[1] *Here's a* stay,] Some of the Commentators think that *stay* means a *hinderer,* and others, a *supporter,* or *partizan.*

I see a yielding in the looks of France;
Mark, how they whisper: urge them, while their souls
Are capable of this ambition:
Lest zeal, now melted, by the windy breath
Of soft petitions, pity, and remorse,
Cool and congeal again to what it was.

1 *Cit.* Why answer not the double majesties
This friendly treaty of our threaten'd town?

K. Phi. Speak England first, that hath been forward first
To speak unto this city: What say you?

K. John. If that the Dauphin there, thy princely son,
Can in this book of beauty read, I love,
Her dowry shall weigh equal with a queen:
For Anjou, and fair Touraine, Maine, Poictiers,
And all that we upon this side the sea
(Except this city now by us besieg'd,)
Find liable to our crown and dignity,
Shall gild her bridal bed; and make her rich
In titles, honours, and promotions,
As she in beauty, education, blood,
Holds hand with any princess of the world.

K. Phi. What say'st thou, boy? look in the lady's face.

Lew. I do, my lord, and in her eye I find
A wonder, or a wondrous miracle,
The shadow of myself form'd in her eye;
Which, being but the shadow of your son,
Becomes a sun, and makes your son a shadow:
I do protest, I never lov'd myself,
Till now infixed I beheld myself,
Drawn in the flattering table of her eye.[2]

[*Whispers with* BLANCH.

[2] Drawn *in the flattering* table *of her eye.*] *Table* is picture, or, rather, the board or canvas on which any object is painted. *Tableau*, Fr.

[Elinor brings Blanch to K John.]

Flourish ready. on Stage

[going a'+ and up to Blanch. - K John retires up a few steps, with K Phil' and Elin' - in conference.]

Heavy Iron Bolt,
and Chains, ready
for noise, - 2-28.-

R. M. B.

Bast. Drawn in the flattering table of her eye!—
Hang'd in the frowning wrinkle of her brow!—
And quarter'd in her heart!—he doth espy
Himself love's traitor: This is pity now,
That hang'd, and drawn, and quarter'd, there should be,
In such a love, so vile a lout as he.

Blanch. My uncle's will, in this respect, is mine.
If he see aught in you, that makes him like,
That any thing he sees, which moves his liking,
I can with ease translate it to my will;
Or, if you will, (to speak more properly,)
I will enforce it easily to my love.
Further I will not flatter you, my lord,
That all I see in you is worthy love,
Than this,—that nothing do I see in you,
(Though churlish thoughts themselves should be your judge,)
That I can find should merit any hate.

K. John. What say these young ones? What say you, my niece?

126:1 *Blanch.* That she is bound in honour still to do
What you in wisdom shall vouchsafe to say.

K. John. Speak then, prince Dauphin; can you love this lady?

Lew. Nay, ask me if I can refrain from love;
For I do love her most unfeignedly.

K. John. Then do I give Volquessen,[3] Touraine, Maine,
Poictiers, and Anjou, these five provinces,
With her to thee; and this addition more,
Full thirty thousand marks of English coin.—
Philip of France, if thou be pleas'd withal,

[3] —— *Volquessen,*] This is the ancient name for the country now called *the Vexin*; in Latin, *Pagus Velocassinus*. That part of it called the *Norman Vexin*, was in dispute between Philip and John.

Command thy son and daughter to join hands.

K. Phi. It likes us well;—Young princes, close your hands.

Aust. And your lips too; for, I am well assur'd,
That I did so, when I was first assur'd.[4]

K. Phi. Now, citizens of Angiers, ope your gates,
Let in that amity which you have made;
For at saint Mary's chapel, presently,
The rites of marriage shall be solemniz'd.—
Is not the lady Constance in this troop?—
I know, she is not; for this match, made up,
Her presence would have interrupted much:—
Where is she and her son? tell me, who knows.

Lew. She is sad and passionate[5] at your highness' tent.

K. Phi. And, by my faith, this league, that we have made,
Will give her sadness very little cure.—
Brother of England, how may we content
This widow lady? In her right we came;
Which we, God knows, have turn'd another way,
To our own vantage.

K. John. We will heal up all,
For we'll create young Arthur duke of Bretagne,
And earl of Richmond; and this rich fair town
We'll make him lord of.—Call the lady Constance;
Some speedy messenger bid her repair
To our solemnity:—I trust we shall,
If not fill up the measure of her will,
Yet in some measure satisfy her so,
That we shall stop her exclamation.

[4] —— *I am well* assur'd,
That I did so, when I was first assur'd.] *Assur'd* is here used both in its common sense, and in an uncommon one, where it signifies *affianced, contracted.*

[5] *She is sad and* passionate —] *Passionate,* in this instance, does not signify *disposed to anger,* but *a prey to mournful sensations.*

§

Flourish. On Stage R/L.

/Lewis eagerly takes Blanch's hand, and kisses it. - The Citizens in great joy and exultation leave the walls, - English and French sheath their their swords, and sling their shields, - then mingle together courteously and friendlily./

/Ads' R.6./

/Ado L 6 in Bland/

Φ /Shelun speaks to Lewis./

Ready for Distant Shouts and Flourish L Ent.

Φ /Exit Salisbury, R.2 E./

Noise of Gates opening, - L. 2 Ent.

Martial Music. - Gates open, - 11 Citizens Enter thro' Gates, bare-headed, - all kneel R. of Gates, - 1st Cit' presents keys, on staff, - Grand March and Procession of the Two powers, in friendly show, thro' Gates, very joyously, thus

Order of Entering Gates.

Flourish and Shouts. Very distant, R.

Go we, as well as haste will suffer us,
To this unlook'd for unprepared pomp.

[*Exeunt all but the* Bastard. — The Citizens retire from the walls.

Bast. Mad world! mad kings! mad composition!
John, to stop Arthur's title in the whole,
Hath willingly departed with a part:[6]
And France, (whose armour conscience buckled on;
Whom zeal and charity brought to the field,
As God's own soldier,) rounded in the ear[7]
With that same purpose-changer, that sly devil;
That broker, that still breaks the pate of faith;
That daily break-vow; he that wins of all,
Of kings, of beggars, old men, young men, maids;—
Who having no external thing to lose
But the word maid,—cheats the poor maid of that;
That smooth-faced gentleman, tickling commodity,—
Commodity, the bias of the world;[8]
The world, who of itself is peised well,
Made to run even, upon even ground;
Till this advantage, this vile drawing bias,
This sway of motion, this commodity,
Makes it take head from all indifferency,
From all direction, purpose, course, intent:
And this same bias, this commodity,
This bawd, this broker, this all-changing word,
Clapp'd on the outward eye of fickle France,
Hath drawn him from his own determin'd aid,
From a resolv'd and honourable war,
To a most base and vile-concluded peace.—
And why rail I on this commodity?

[6] —— departed *with a part:*] To *part* and to *depart* were formerly synonymous.

[7] —— rounded *in the ear* —] i. e. whispered in the ear.

[8] Commodity, *the* bias *of the world;*] *Commodity* is interest.

But for because he hath not woo'd me yet:
Not that I have the power to clutch my hand,
When his fair angels would salute my palm:
But for[9] my hand, as unattempted yet,
Like a poor beggar, raileth on the rich.
Well, whiles I am a beggar, I will rail,
And say,—there is no sin, but to be rich;
And being rich, my virtue then shall be,
To say,—there is no vice, but beggary:
Since kings break faith upon commodity,
Gain, be my lord! for I will worship thee! [Exit.

ACT III.

SCENE I. *The same. The French King's Tent.*

Enter CONSTANCE, ARTHUR, *and* SALISBURY.

Const. Gone to be married! gone to swear a peace!
False blood to false blood join'd! Gone to be friends!
Shall Lewis have Blanch? and Blanch those provinces?
It is not so; thou hast misspoke, misheard;
Be well advis'd, tell o'er thy tale again:
It cannot be; thou dost but say, 'tis so:
I trust, I may not trust thee; for thy word
Is but the vain breath of a common man:
Believe me, I do not believe thee, man;
I have a king's oath to the contrary.
Thou shalt be punish'd for thus frighting me,
For I am sick, and capable of fears;[1]

[9] *But for*—] i. e. because.

[1] *For I am sick, and capable of fears;*] i. e. I have a strong *sensibility;* I am tremblingly alive to apprehension.

Stop Shouts, &c.

Shouts, &c. — (rep.d) (very faint!)

Oppress'd with wrongs, and therefore full of fears;
A widow, husbandless, subject to fears;
A woman, naturally born to fears;
And though thou now confess, thou didst but jest,
With my vex'd spirits I cannot take a truce,
But they will quake and tremble all this day.
What dost thou mean by shaking of thy head?
Why dost thou look so sadly on my son?
What means that hand upon that breast of thine?
Why holds thine eye that lamentable rheum,
Like a proud river peering o'er its bounds?
Be these sad signs confirmers of thy words?
Then speak again; not all thy former tale,
But this one word, whether thy tale be true.

Sal. As true, as, I believe, you think them false,
That give you cause to prove my saying true.

Const. O, if thou teach me to believe this sorrow,
Teach thou this sorrow how to make me die;
And let belief and life encounter so,
As doth the fury of two desperate men,
Which, in the very meeting, fall, and die.—
Lewis marry Blanch! O, boy, then where art thou?
France friend with England! what becomes of me?—
Fellow, be gone; I cannot brook thy sight;
This news hath made thee a most ugly man.

Sal. What other harm have I, good lady, done,
But spoke the harm that is by others done?

Const. Which harm within itself so heinous is,
As it makes harmful all that speak of it.

Arth. I do beseech you, madam, be content.

Const. If thou, that bid'st me be content, wert grim,
Ugly, and sland'rous to thy mother's womb,
Full of unpleasing blots, and sightless[2] stains,

[2] —— *sightless* —] The poet uses *sightless* for that which we now express by *unsightly*, disagreeable to the eyes.

Lame, foolish, crooked, swart,[3] prodigious,[4]
Patch'd with foul moles, and eye-offending marks,
I would not care, I then would be content;
For then I should not love thee; no, nor thou
Become thy great birth, nor deserve a crown.
But thou art fair; and at thy birth, dear boy!
Nature and fortune join'd to make thee great:
Of nature's gifts thou may'st with lilies boast,
And with the half-blown rose: but fortune, O!
She is corrupted, chang'd, and won from thee;
She adulterates hourly with thine uncle John;
And with her golden hand hath pluck'd on France
To tread down fair respect of sovereignty,
And made his majesty the bawd to theirs.
France is a bawd to fortune, and king John;
That strumpet fortune, that usurping John:—
Tell me, thou fellow, is not France forsworn?
Envenom him with words; or get thee gone,
And leave these woes alone, which I alone,
Am bound to under-bear.

Sal. Pardon me, madam,
I may not go without you to the kings.

Const. Thou may'st, thou shalt, I will not go with thee:
I will instruct my sorrows to be proud;
For grief is proud, and makes his owner stout.
To me, and to the state of my great grief,
Let kings assemble;[5] for my grief's so great,

[3] —— *swart,*] *Swart* is brown, inclining to black.

[4] —— *prodigious,*] That is, *portentous,* so deformed as to be taken for a *foretoken of evil.*

[5] *To me, and to the state of my great grief,*
Let kings assemble;] In *Much Ado about Nothing,* the father of Hero, depressed by her disgrace, declares himself so subdued by grief, that a *thread may lead him.* How is it that grief, in Leonato and Lady Constance, produces effects directly opposite, and yet both agreeable to nature? Sorrow softens the mind while it is yet warmed by hope, but hardens it when it is congealed by

Flourish ready
L.U.E.

/X'es to R. Arthur follows her./

/putting Arth' to her R./

Heralds enter & Attend[ants] place chairs on Dais

Flourish of Trumpets

L.U.E. — who march on

And the whole of the French and English parties, - Nobles - Knights - Esquires, - Heralds, - &c - &c - The Attendants place the other chair on the Dais.

Elin. Faulc. K. John (seated) Lewis. Blanch. K. Phil. Const. Arth. Aust.

R. L.

Trumpet ready - R.U.E.

That no supporter but the huge firm earth
Can hold it up: here I and sorrow sit;
Here is my throne, bid kings come bow to it. *Pause*
[*She throws herself on the ground,* R.C.

Enter King JOHN, *King* PHILIP, LEWIS, BLANCH, ELINOR, Bastard, AUSTRIA, *and Attendants.*

K. Phi. 'Tis true, fair daughter; and this blessed day,
Ever in France shall be kept festival:
To solemnize this day, the glorious sun
Stays in his course, and plays the alchemist;
Turning, with splendor of his precious eye,
The meagre cloddy earth to glittering gold:
The yearly course, that brings this day about,
Shall never see it but a holyday.

Const. A wicked day, and not a holyday!—— [*Rising.*
What hath this day deserv'd? what hath it done;
That it in golden letters should be set,
Among the high tides,[6] in the kalendar?
Nay, rather, turn this day out of the week;
This day of shame, oppression, perjury:
Or, if it must stand still, let wives with child
Pray, that their burdens may not fall this day,
Lest that their hopes prodigiously be cross'd:[7]
But on this day,[8] let seamen fear no wreck;

despair. Distress, while there remains any prospect of relief, is weak and flexible, but when no succour remains, is fearless and stubborn; angry alike at those that injure, and at those that do not help; careless to please where nothing can be gained, and fearless to offend when there is nothing further to be dreaded. Such was this writer's knowledge of the passions.

[6] —— *high tides,*] i. e. solemn seasons.

[7] —— prodigiously *be cross'd:*] i. e. be disappointed by the production of a prodigy, a monster.

[8] *But on this day,*] That is, *except* on this day.

~~No bargains break, that are not this day made:~~
This day, all things begun come to ill end;
Yea, faith itself to hollow falsehood change!

K. Phi. By heaven, lady, you shall have no cause
To curse the fair proceedings of this day:
Have I not pawn'd to you my majesty?

Const. You have beguil'd me with a counterfeit,
Resembling majesty; which, being touch'd, and tried,
Proves valueless: You are forsworn, forsworn;
You came in arms to spill mine enemies' blood,
But now in arms you strengthen it with yours:
The grappling vigour and rough frown of war,
Is cold in amity and painted peace,
And our oppression hath made up this league:— Ф
Arm, arm, you heavens, against these perjur'd kings!
A widow cries; be husband to me, heavens!
Let not the hours of this ungodly day
Wear out the day in peace; but, ere sunset,
Set armed discord 'twixt these perjur'd kings!
Hear me, O, hear me! Hear me

|R| *Aust.* Lady Constance, peace.

Const. War! war! no peace! peace is to me a war.
O Lymoges! O Austria![9] thou dost shame

[9] *O* Lymoges! *O* Austria!] The propriety or impropriety of these titles, which every editor has suffered to pass unnoted, deserves a little consideration. Shakspeare has, on this occasion, followed the old play, which at once furnished him with the character of Faulconbridge, and ascribed the death of Richard I. to the duke of Austria. In the person of Austria he has conjoined the two well-known enemies of Cœur-de-lion. Leopold, duke of Austria, threw him into prison, in a former expedition; [in 1193] but the castle of Chaluz, before which he fell [in 1199] belonged to Vidomar, viscount of Limoges; and the archer who pierced his shoulder with an arrow (of which wound he died) was Bertrand de Gourdon. The editors seem hitherto to have understood *Lymoges* as being an appendage to the title of Austria, and therefore enquired no further about it.

Ф / K Phil goes up to the Dais, and sits. /

/ goes to L, and, then, up, a little /

That bloody spoil: Thou slave, thou wretch, thou coward;
Thou little valiant, great in villainy!
Thou ever strong upon the stronger side!
Thou fortune's champion, that dost never fight
But when her humorous ladyship is by
To teach thee safety! thou art perjur'd too,
And sooth'st up greatness. What a fool art thou,
A ramping fool; to brag, and stamp, and swear,
Upon my party! Thou cold-blooded slave,
Hast thou not spoke like thunder on my side?
Been sworn my soldier? bidding me depend
Upon thy stars, thy fortune, and thy strength?
And dost thou now fall over to my foes?
Thou wear a lion's hide! doff it for shame,
And hang a calf's-skin on those recreant limbs.

Aust. O, that a man should speak those words to me!

Bast. And hang a calf's-skin on those recreant limbs.

Aust. Thou dar'st not say so, villain, for thy life.

Bast. And hang a calf's-skin on those recreant limbs.

K. John. We like not this; thou dost forget thyself.

Enter PANDULPH,

K. Phi. Here comes the holy legate of the pope.

Pand. Hail, you anointed deputies of heaven!—
To thee, King John, my holy errand is.
I Pandulph, of fair Milan cardinal,
And from pope Innocent the legate here,
Do, in his name, religiously demand,
Why thou against the church, our holy mother,
So wilfully dost spurn; and, force perforce,
Keep Stephen Langton, chosen archbishop

Of Canterbury, from that holy see?
This, in our 'foresaid holy father's name,
Pope Innocent, I do demand of thee.
K. John. What earthly name to interrogatories,
Can task the free breath[1] of a sacred king?
Thou canst not, cardinal, devise a name
So slight, unworthy, and ridiculous,
To charge me to an answer, as the pope.
Tell him this tale; and from the mouth of England,
Add thus much more,—That no Italian priest
Shall tithe or toll in our dominions;
But as we under heaven are supreme head,
So, under him, that great supremacy,
Where we do reign, we will alone uphold,
Without the assistance of a mortal hand:
So tell the pope; all reverence set apart,
To him, and his usurp'd authority. ⌀
K. Phi. Brother of England, you blaspheme in this.
K. John. Though you, and all the kings of Christendom,
Are led so grossly by this meddling priest,
Dreading the curse that money may buy out;
And, by the merit of vile gold, dross, dust,
Purchase corrupted pardon of a man,
Who, in that sale, sells pardon from himself:
Though you, and all the rest, so grossly led,
This juggling witchcraft with revenue cherish;
Yet I, alone, alone do me oppose
Against the pope, and count his friends my foes.
/up R/ *Pand.* Then, by the lawful power that I have,
Thou shalt stand curs'd, and excommunicate: ⌀

[1] *What* earthly *name to interrogatories,*
Can task *the free* breath, *&c.*] i. e. What earthly name, *subjoined* to interrogatories, can force a king to *speak* and answer them?

⌀ /All appear alarmed at K. John's temerity./

⌀ /Shudder, and sensation of fear and horror thro' the assembly./

/Going up to Pandulph./

And blessed shall he be, that doth revolt
From his allegiance to an heretick;
And meritorious shall that hand be call'd,
~~Canonized, and worship'd as a saint,~~
That takes away by any secret course
Thy hateful life.

Const. O, lawful let it be,
That I have room with Rome to curse a while!
Good father cardinal, cry thou, amen,
To my keen curses: for, without my wrong,
There is no tongue hath power to curse him right.

Pand. There's law and warrant, lady, for my curse.

Const. And for mine too; when law can do no right,
Let it be lawful, that law bar no wrong:
Law cannot give my child his kingdom here;
For he, that holds his kingdom, holds the law:
Therefore, since law itself is perfect wrong,
How can the law forbid my tongue to curse?

Pand. Philip of France, on peril of a curse,
Let go the hand of that arch-heretick;
And raise the power of France upon his head,
Unless he do submit himself to Rome.

Eli. Look'st thou pale, France? do not let go thy hand.

Const. Look to that, devil! lest that France repent,
And, by disjoining hands, hell lose a soul.

Aust. King Philip, listen to the cardinal.

Bast. And hang a calf's-skin on his recreant limbs.

Aust. Well, ruffian, I must pocket up these wrongs,
Because——

Bast. Your breeches best may carry them.

K. John. Philip, what say'st thou to the cardinal?

Const. What should he say, but as the cardinal?

Lew. Bethink you, father; for the difference
Is, purchase of a heavy curse from Rome,
Or the light loss of England for a friend:
Forgo the easier.

Blanch. That's the curse of Rome.

Const. O Lewis, stand fast; the devil tempts thee here,
In likeness of a new untrimmed bride.[2]

Blanch. The lady Constance speaks not from her faith,
But from her need.

Const. O, if thou grant my need,
Which only lives but by the death of faith,
That need must needs infer this principle,——
That faith would live again by death of need;
O, then, tread down my need, and faith mounts up;
Keep my need up, and faith is trodden down.

K. John. The king is mov'd, and answers not to this.

Const. O, be remov'd from him, and answer well.

Aust. Do so, king Philip; hang no more in doubt.

Bast. Hang nothing but a calf's-skin, most sweet lout.

K. Phi. I am perplex'd, and know not what to say.

Pand. What can'st thou say, but will perplex thee more,
If thou stand excommunicate, and curs'd?

K. Phi. Good reverend father, make my person yours,
And tell me, how you would bestow yourself.
This royal hand and mine are newly knit;
And the conjunction of our inward souls

[2] —— *a new* untrimmed *bride.*] i. e. *undressed.*

Married in league, coupled and link'd together
With all religious strength of sacred vows;
The latest breath that gave the sound of words,
Was deep-sworn faith, peace, amity, true love,
Between our kingdoms, and our royal selves;
And even before this truce, but new before,—
No longer than we well could wash our hands,
To clap this royal bargain up of peace,—
Heaven knows, they were besmear'd and overstain'd
With slaughter's pencil; where revenge did paint
The fearful difference of incensed kings:
And shall these hands, so lately purg'd of blood,
So newly join'd in love, so strong in both,
Unyoke this seizure, and this kind regreet?[3]
Play fast and loose with faith? so jest with heaven,
Make such unconstant children of ourselves,
As now again to snatch our palm from palm;
Unswear faith sworn; and on the marriage bed
Of smiling peace to march a bloody host,
And make a riot on the gentle brow
Of true sincerity? O holy sir,
My reverend father, let it not be so:
Out of your grace, devise, ordain, impose
Some gentle order; and then we shall be bless'd
To do your pleasure, and continue friends.

Pand. All form is formless, order orderless,
Save what is opposite to England's love.
Therefore, to arms! be champion of our church!
Or let the church, our mother, breathe her curse,
A mother's curse, on her revolting son.
France, thou may'st hold a serpent by the tongue,
A cased lion by the mortal paw,
A fasting tiger safer by the tooth,
Than keep in peace that hand which thou dost hold. ф

K. Phi. I may disjoin my hand, but not my faith.

[3] —— *this kind* regreet?] A *regreet* is an exchange of salutation.

ф /English party, watching with intense anxiety, the French King.- Strong deprecating action, by the French and Austrians./

Pand. So mak'st thou faith an enemy to faith;
And, like a civil war, set'st oath to oath,
Thy tongue against thy tongue. O, let thy vow
First made to heaven, first be to heaven perform'd;
That is, to be the champion of our church!
What since thou swor'st, is sworn against thyself,
And may not be performed by thyself:
For that, which thou hast sworn to do amiss,
Is not amiss when it is truly done;[4]
And being not done, where doing tends to ill,
The truth is then most done not doing it:
The better act of purposes mistook
Is, to mistake again; though indirect,
Yet indirection thereby grows direct,
And falsehood falsehood cures; as fire cools fire,
Within the scorched veins of one new burn'd.
It is religion, that doth make vows kept;
But thou hast sworn against religion;
By what thou swear'st, against the thing thou swear'st;
And mak'st an oath the surety for thy truth
Against an oath: The truth thou art unsure
To swear, swear only not to be forsworn;
Else, what a mockery should it be to swear?
But thou dost swear only to be forsworn;
And most forsworn, to keep what thou dost swear.
Therefore, thy latter vows, against thy first,
Is in thyself rebellion to thyself:
And better conquest never canst thou make,
Than arm thy constant and thy nobler parts
Against those giddy loose suggestions:

[4] Is not *amiss, when it is truly done;*] i. e. *that,* which you have sworn to *do amiss,* is *not amiss,* (i. e. becomes right) when it is *done truly* (that is, as he explains it, not done at all;) and being *not done,* where it would be a *sin* to *do it,* the *truth* is *most done* when you *do it not:* Other parts of this speech have puzzled the commentators, who have, in turn, puzzled their readers.

Trumpets and Drums, ready for Alarums, R. ~~and L.~~

[The French greatly excited.]

[Lewis goes up to C, Blanch follows him.]

Upon which better part our prayers come in,
If thou vouchsafe them: but, if not, then know,
The peril of our curses light on thee;
So heavy, as thou shalt not shake them off,
But, in despair, die under their black weight.

Aust. Rebellion, flat rebellion!

Bast. Will't not be?
Will not a calf's-skin stop that mouth of thine?

Lew. Father, to arms!

Blanch. Upon thy wedding day?
Against the blood that thou hast married?
What, shall our feast be kept with slaughter'd men?
Shall braying trumpets, and loud churlish drums,—
Clamours of hell,—be measures[5] to our pomp?
O husband, hear me!—ah, alack, how new
Is husband in my mouth!—even for that name,
Which till this time my tongue did ne'er pronounce,
Upon my knee I beg, go not to arms
Against mine uncle.

Const. O, upon my knee,
Made hard with kneeling, I do pray to thee,
Thou virtuous Dauphin, alter not the doom
Fore-thought by heaven.

Blanch. Now shall I see thy love; What motive may
Be stronger with thee than the name of wife?

Const. That which upholdeth him that thee upholds,
His honour: O, thine honour, Lewis, thine honour!

Lew. I muse,[6] your majesty doth seem so cold,
When such profound respects do pull you on.

Pand. I will denounce a curse upon his head.

[5] —— *be measures*—] The *measures*, it has already been more than once observed, were a species of solemn dance in our author's time.

[6] *I muse,*] i. e. I wonder.

K. Phi. Thou shalt not need:—England, I'll fall from thee. Ø

Const. O fair return of banish'd majesty!

~~*Eli.* O foul revolt of French inconstancy!~~

K. John. France, thou shalt rue this hour within this hour. /rising./

~~*Bast.* Old time the clock-setter, that bald sexton time,~~
~~Is it as he will? well then, France shall rue.~~

~~*Blanch.* The sun's o'ercast with blood: Fair day, adieu!~~
~~Which is the side that I must go withal?~~
~~I am with both: each army hath a hand;~~
~~And, in their rage, I having hold of both,~~
~~They whirl asunder, and dismember me.~~
~~Husband, I cannot pray that thou may'st win;~~
~~Uncle, I needs must pray that thou may'st lose;~~
~~Father, I may not wish the fortune thine;~~
~~Grandam, I will not wish thy wishes thrive:~~
~~Whoever wins, on that side shall I lose;~~
~~Assured loss, before the match be play'd.~~

~~*Lew.* Lady, with me; with me thy fortune lies.~~

~~*Blanch.* There where my fortune lives, there my life dies.~~

K. John. Cousin, go draw our puissance together.— [*Exit* Bastard, L.B./

/advances L.B./ - France, I am burn'd up with inflaming wrath;
A rage, whose heat hath this condition,
Than nothing can allay, nothing but blood,
The blood, and dearest-valu'd blood, of France.

K. Phi. ~~Thy rage shall burn thee up, and thou shalt turn~~
~~To ashes, ere our blood shall quench that fire:~~
Look to thyself, thou art in jeopardy.

K. John. No more than he that threats.—To arms let's hie! [*Exeunt.*

/Tumult, ~~discordant cries and orders~~, - the English Exeunt, first, - L.B. - followed by the French, &c. - Noise of Battle heard, as Scene changes. - Alarums, Drums &c are continued without intermission, sometimes nearer and louder, sometimes more distant. /

Ø /K Phil' leaves the throne, and X'es to R.B. - General excitement and movement, - Nobles bracing on their shields, preparing for battle, X R and L, - and crowd round their respective Kings, - Engh L. - Frch, - R. - /

Alarums, - Drums & Trumpets

W. - /quick! - to close in, at 1 Gr./

At change of Sc. French and English Nobles, &c. pass a X R & L. as in pursuit, and retreat, thus. 1st Group, Neuville, Beaumont, and 2 French Barons, - 2nd D°. Blois, Fitzwalter, & 2 Fr. Attendants. 3rd D°. Pembroke, Norfolk and 2 Engh Knights, - all rapidly X L to R. - Oxford, R to L. - 6 Austrian Knts L to R. The Bastard L (Now, by my life! &c) meeting Austria, R. Short rapid combat, off R. followed by Essex, Percy, and 3 English Esquires in pursuit L to R, and off. - Re-enter Bastard R. with the Lion's hide, - (Austria's head &c) - he throws the hide, off R. as he speaks, - Hubert, - with Essex and his party re-enter R, meeting K John, L. with Prince Arthur - De Ros, Clare, Arundel, and Hereford. - Pembroke, Norfolk & Fitzwalter, also, re-enter R. - and Oxford, L. at same time.

Flourish & ~~Shouts~~
do — do

K John throws Arth. a X to Hub. who X es with him, rapidly, to the L. and Exit's.

Alarums, ~~Shouts~~, &c

Which gradually subside, and through which various Trumpet Calls are heard, answering each other, - then a Retreat is sounded - During which the Scene changes.

W.

Essex, Norfolk, Fitzwalter, and Percy, Enter R.U.E. and go slowly - as tho' fatigued - to L.2E. then Pembroke - followed by Oxford - Arundel - and 2 English Knights, who go down R. in same manner, - 4 Esquires precede K John, who is speaking to the Queen Mother, as they both enter, - after them, Hubert, with Arthur - and lastly the Bastard.

Borders down Sc 3

SCENE II.

The same. Plains near Angiers. /1 Gr./

Alarums, Excursions. Enter the Bastard, ~~*with* Austria's Head~~. /L./

Bast. Now, by my life, this day grows wondrous hot;
Some airy devil hovers in the sky,
And pours down mischief. Austria's head lie there;
While Philip breathes.

/Enter Austria R. Fight, and off R. Essex &c enter &c. Re-enter Bast. with skin./

Enter King JOHN, ARTHUR, ~~and~~ HUBERT, &c R. /&c L./

2 Knts
Essex
Fitzwalter
Arundel
De Ros

K. John. Hubert, keep this boy:—Philip, make up:
My mother is assailed in our tent,
And ta'en, I fear. /going L./

Bast. My lord, I rescu'd her;
Her highness is in safety, fear you not:
But on, my liege; for very little pains
Will bring this labour to an happy end. [*Exeunt*, L. rapidly.]

SCENE III.

/3 G./ - *The same.*

Give time before the change of Scene.

~~*Alarums, Excursions*~~; *Retreat. Enter King* JOHN, ELINOR, ARTHUR, *the* Bastard, HUBERT, *and* Lords. /R; U.E./

K. John. So shall it be; your grace shall stay behind, [*To* ELINOR, R.]
So strongly guarded.—Cousin, look not sad: [Goes - *To* ARTHUR, L.]

Thy grandam loves thee; and thy uncle will
As dear be to thee as thy father was.

Arth. O, this will make my mother die with
grief. /weeps violently./

K. John. Cousin, [*To the* Bastard.] away for
England; haste before:
And, ere our coming, see thou shake the bags
Of hoarding abbots; angels imprisoned
Set thou at liberty: the fat ribs of peace
Must by the hungry now be fed upon:
Use our commission in his utmost force.

Bast. Bell, book, and candle[7] shall not drive me
back,
When gold and silver becks me to come on.
I leave your highness:—Grandam, I will pray
(If ever I remember to be holy,)
For your fair safety; so I kiss your hand.

Eli. Farewell, my gentle cousin.

K. John. Coz, farewell.

[*Exit* Bastard, L.-/

Eli. Come hither, little kinsman; hark, a word.

[*She takes* ARTHUR *aside*./

K. John. Come hither, Hubert. O my gentle
Hubert,
We owe thee much; within this wall of flesh
There is a soul, counts thee her creditor,
And with advantage means to pay thy love:
And, my good friend, thy voluntary oath
Lives in this bosom, dearly cherished.
Give me thy hand. I had a thing to say,—
But I will fit it with some better time.
By heaven, Hubert, I am almost asham'd
To say what good respect I have of thee.

Hub. I am much bounden to your majesty.

7 Bell, book, *and* candle—] In an account of the Romish curse given by Dr. Grey, it appears that three candles were extinguished, one by one, in different parts of the execration.

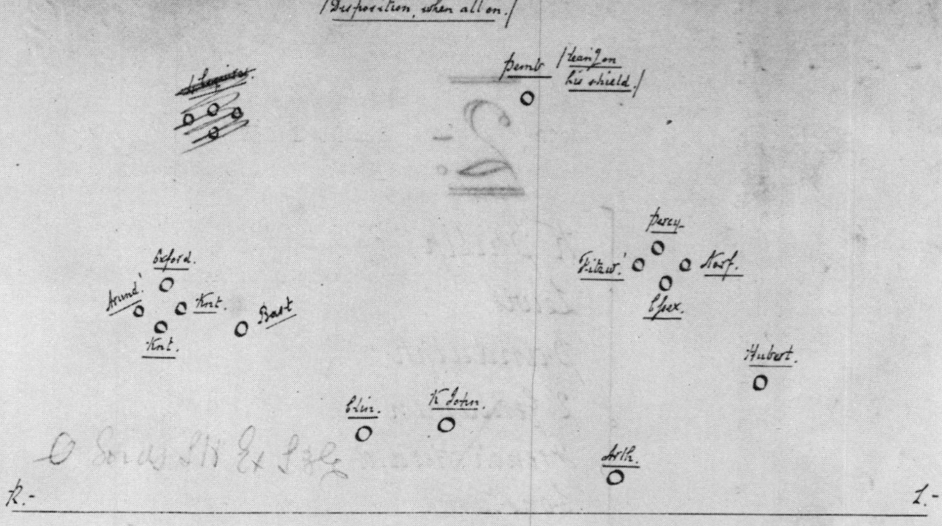

ϕ /Bast' stops at L-1E.- and turns to the King./

/Arth' - wiping his eyes, - X'es to the Queen, - as he X'es, Hubert goes down, as tho' undesignedly to the front, L.- The Nobles confer, in groupes, and no face on the stage except the King's and Hubert's, is turned to the audience, during the ensuing dialogue./

2.

K Philip.
Lewis.
Pandulph.
2 Gentlemen
French Herald.
Constance.
2 Ladies.

Trumpets ready 1.
distant!

2.

K. John. Good friend, thou hast no cause to say so yet:
But thou shalt have; and creep time ne'er so slow,
Yet it shall come, for me to do thee good.
I had a thing to say,—But let it go:
The sun is in the heaven, and the proud day,
Attended with the pleasures of the world,
Is all too wanton, and too full of gawds,[8]
To give me audience:—If the midnight bell
Did, with his iron tongue and brazen mouth,
Sound one unto the drowsy race of night;
If this same were a church-yard where we stand,
And thou possessed with a thousand wrongs;
Or if that surly spirit, melancholy,
Had bak'd thy blood, and made it heavy, thick;
(Which, else, runs tickling up and down the veins,
Making that idiot, laughter, keep men's eyes,
And strain their cheeks to idle merriment,
A passion hateful to my purposes;)
Or if that thou could'st see me without eyes,
Hear me without thine ears, and make reply
Without a tongue, using conceit alone,[9]
Without eyes, ears, and harmful sound of words;
Then, in despite of brooded watchful day,
I would into thy bosom pour my thoughts:
But ah, I will not:—Yet I love thee well;
And, by my troth, I think, thou lov'st me well.

Hub. So well, that what you bid me undertake,
Though that my death were adjunct to my act,
By heaven, I'd do't.

K. John. Do not I know, thou would'st?
Good Hubert, Hubert, Hubert, throw thine eye
On yon young boy: I'll tell thee what, my friend,
He is a very serpent in my way;

[8] —— *full of* gawds,] *Gawds* are any showy ornaments.

[9] —— *using* conceit *alone,*] *Conceit* here, as in many other places, signifies *conception,* thought.

And, wheresoe'er this foot of mine doth tread,
He lies before me: Dost thou understand me?
Thou art his keeper.

Hub. And I will keep him so,
That he shall not offend your majesty.

K. John. Death.

Hub. My lord?

K. John. A grave.

Hub. He shall not live.

K. John. Enough.
I could be merry now: Hubert, I love thee;
Well, I'll not say what I intend for thee:
Remember.[1]——Madam, fare you well:
I'll send those powers o'er to your majesty.

Eli. My blessing go with thee!

K. John. For England, cousin:
Hubert shall be your man, attend on you
With all true duty.—On toward Calais, ho!

[*Exeunt*, L.-]

SCENE IV.

The same. The French King's Tent.

Enter King Philip, Lewis, Pandulph, *and* 2 Gentlemen, and French Herald. Attendants

K. Phi. So, by a roaring tempest on the flood,
A whole armado of convicted sail[2]
Is scatter'd and disjoin'd from fellowship.

Pand. Courage and comfort! all shall yet go well.

[1] *Remember.*] This is one of the scenes to which may be promised a lasting commendation. Art could add little to its perfection; no change in dramatick taste can injure it; and time itself can subtract nothing from its beauties.

[2] —— *of* convicted *sail*—] Overpowered, baffled, destroyed.

Reenter Nobles L.H.

/All turn - quietly - to the front. - The Knights advance, R.- Hub' X'es to Arth' R.-/

/Embraces John, and Exit's R.- preceded by the 2 Knts, foll'd by 4 Esquires./

25

Flow Trumpet March - L- /dist.t/

/Nobles, on L,- precede K John, and Exit L,- others follow, - Hubert and Arthur last - Arth weeps./

K. Phi. What can go well, when we have run so ill?
Are we not beaten? Is not Angiers lost?
Arthur ta'en prisoner? divers dear friends slain?
And bloody England into England gone,
O'erbearing interruption, spite of France?
Lew. What he hath won, that hath he fortified:
So hot a speed with such advice dispos'd,
Such temperate order in so fierce a cause,
Doth want example: Who hath read, or heard,
Of any kindred action like to this?
K. Phi. Well could I bear that England had this praise,
So we could find some pattern of our shame.

Enter CONSTANCE,

Look, who comes here! a grave unto a soul;
Holding the eternal spirit, against her will,
In the vile prison of afflicted breath:—
I pr'ythee, lady, go away with me.
Const. Lo, now! now see the issue of your peace!
K. Phi. Patience, good lady! comfort, gentle Constance!
Const. No, I defy[3] all counsel, all redress,
But that which ends all counsel, true redress,
Death, death:—O amiable lovely death!
Thou odoriferous stench! sound rottenness!
Arise forth from the couch of lasting night,
Thou hate and terror to prosperity,
And I will kiss thy détestable bones;
And put my eye-balls in thy vaulty brows;
And ring these fingers with thy household worms;
And stop this gap of breath with fulsome dust,

[3] *No, I defy, &c.*] To *defy* anciently signified to *refuse*.

~~And be a carrion monster like thyself~~:
Come, grin on me; and I will think thou smil'st,
And buss thee as thy wife! Misery's love,[4]
O, come to me!

K. Phi. O fair affliction, peace.

Const. No, no, I will not, having breath to cry:—
O, that my tongue were in the thunder's mouth!
Then with a passion would I shake the world;
And rouse from sleep that fell anatomy,
Which cannot hear a lady's feeble voice,
Which scorns a modern invocation.[5]

Pand. Lady, you utter madness, and not sorrow.

Const. Thou art not holy to belie me so;
I am not mad: this hair I tear, is mine;
My name is Constance; I was Geffrey's wife;
Young Arthur is my son, and he is lost: lost: lost:
I am not mad;—I would to heaven, I were!
For then, 'tis like I should forget myself:
O, if I could, what grief should I forget!—
Preach some philosophy to make me mad,
And thou shalt be canoniz'd, cardinal;
~~For, being not mad, but sensible of grief,~~
My reasonable part produces reason
How I may be deliver'd of these woes,
~~And teaches me to kill or hang myself:~~
If I were mad, I should forget my son;
~~Or madly think, a babe of clouts were he.~~
I am not mad; too well, too well I feel
The different plague of each calamity.

K. Phi. Bind up those tresses:[6] ~~O, what love I note~~

[4] *Misery's love, &c.*] Thou, death, who art *courted* by *Misery* to come to his relief, O come to me.

[5] —— modern *invocation.*] i. e. trite, common.

[6] *Bind up those tresses:*] It was necessary that Constance should be interrupted; because a passion so violent cannot be borne

/Lewis ~~goes up, and~~ leans, dejectedly, ~~on table~~, R./

In the fair multitude of those her hairs!
Where but by chance a silver drop hath fallen,
Even to that drop ten thousand wiry friends
Do glew themselves in sociable grief;
Like true, inseparable, faithful loves,
Sticking together in calamity.

Const. To England, if you will.

K. Phi. Bind up your hairs.

Const. Yes, that I will; And wherefore will I do it?
I tore them from their bonds; and cried aloud,
O that these hands could so redeem my son,
As they have given these hairs their liberty!
But now I envy at their liberty,
And will again commit them to their bonds,
Because my poor child is a prisoner.—
And, father cardinal, I have heard you say,
That we shall see and know our friends in heaven:
If that be true, I shall see my boy again;
For, since the birth of Cain, the first male child,
To him that did but yesterday suspire,[7]
There was not such a gracious creature born.[8]
But now will canker sorrow eat my bud,
And chase the native beauty from his cheek,
And he will look as hollow as a ghost;
As dim and meagre as an ague's fit;
And so he'll die; and, rising so again,
When I shall meet him in the court of heaven
I shall not know him: therefore never, never
Must I behold my pretty Arthur more.

Pand. You hold too heinous a respect of grief.

Const. He talks to me, that never had a son.

long. I wish the following speeches had been equally happy; but they only serve to show how difficult it is to maintain the pathetick long. JOHNSON.

[7] —— *but yesterday* suspire,] i. e. breathe.

[8] —— *a* gracious *creature born.*] *Gracious*, i. e. *graceful*.

K. Phi. You are as fond of grief, as of your child.
Const. Grief fills the room up of my absent child,
Lies in his bed, walks up and down with me;
Puts on his pretty looks, repeats his words,
Remembers me of all his gracious parts,
Stuffs out his vacant garments with his form;
Then, have I reason to be fond of grief.
Fare you well: had you such a loss as I,
I could give better comfort[9] than you do.—
I will not keep this form upon my head,
[*Tearing off her head-dress.*
When there is such disorder in my wit.
O lord! my boy, my Arthur, my fair son!
My life, my joy, my food, my all the world!
My widow-comfort, and my sorrows' cure! [*Exit.*
K. Phi. I fear some outrage, and I'll follow her.
[*Exit.*

Lew. There's nothing in this world, can make me joy:[1]
Life is as tedious as a twice-told tale,
Vexing the dull ear of a drowsy man;
And bitter shame hath spoil'd the sweet world's taste,
That it yields naught, but shame, and bitterness.
Pand. Before the curing of a strong disease,
Even in the instant of repair and health,
The fit is strongest; evils, that take leave,

9 —— *had you such a loss as I,*
I could give better comfort—] This is a sentiment which great sorrow always dictates. Whoever cannot help himself casts his eyes on others for assistance, and often mistakes their inability for coldness. JOHNSON.

1 *There's nothing in this,* &c.] The young prince feels his defeat with more sensibility than his father. Shame operates most strongly in the earlier years; and when can disgrace be less welcome than when a man is going to his bride? JOHNSON.

ф Pandulph retires up

R.H.1 E. ф ~~This tent and off L. the Ladies follow.~~

R.H.1 E. ~~thro' tent, off L.~~

R. M. B.

On their departure most of all show evil:
What have you lost by losing of this day?
Lew. All days of glory, joy, and happiness.
Pand. If you have won it, certainly, you had.
No, no: when fortune means to men most good,
She looks upon them with a threatening eye.
'Tis strange, to think how much king John hath lost
In this which he accounts so clearly won:
Are not you griev'd, that Arthur is his prisoner?
Lew. As heartily, as he is glad he hath him.
Pand. Your mind is all as youthful as your blood.
Now hear me speak, with a prophetick spirit;
For even the breath of what I mean to speak
Shall blow each dust, each straw, each little rub,
Out of the path which shall directly lead
Thy foot to England's throne; and, therefore, mark.
John hath seiz'd Arthur; and it cannot be,
That, whiles warm life plays in that infant's veins,
The misplac'd John should entertain an hour,
One minute, nay, one quiet breath of rest:
A scepter, snatch'd with an unruly hand,
Must be as boisterously maintain'd as gain'd:
And he, that stands upon a slippery place,
Makes nice of no vile hold to stay him up:
That John may stand, then Arthur needs must fall;
So be it, for it cannot be but so.
Lew. But what shall I gain by young Arthur's fall?
Pand. You, in the right of lady Blanch your wife,
May then make all the claim that Arthur did.
Lew. And lose it, life and all, as Arthur did.
Pand. How green are you, and fresh in this old world!

John lays you plots; the times conspire with you:
For he, that steeps his safety in true blood,
Shall find but bloody safety, and untrue.
This act, so evilly born, shall cool the hearts
Of all his people, and freeze up their zeal;
That none so small advantage shall step forth,
To check his reign, but they will cherish it:
No natural exhalation in the sky,
No scape of nature, no distemper'd day,
No common wind, no customed event,
But they will pluck away his natural cause,
And call them meteors, prodigies, and signs,
Abortives, présages, and tongues of heaven,
Plainly denouncing vengeance upon John.

Lew. May be, he will not touch young Arthur's life,
But hold himself safe in his prisonment.

Pand. O, sir, when he shall hear of your approach,
If that young Arthur be not gone already,
Even at that news he dies: and then the hearts
Of all his people shall revolt from him,
And kiss the lips of unacquainted change,
And pick strong matter of revolt, and wrath,
Out of the bloody fingers' ends of John.
Methinks, I see this hurly all on foot;
And, O, what better matter breeds for you,
Than I have nam'd!—The bastard Faulconbridge
Is now in England, ransacking the church,
Offending charity: If but a dozen French
Were there in arms, they would be as a call
To train ten thousand English to their side;
Or, as a little snow, tumbled about,
Anon becomes a mountain. ✠ O noble Dauphin,
Go with me to the king: 'Tis wonderful,
What may be wrought out of their discontent:
Now that their souls are topfull of offence,

✠ /Lewis animated./

Time, Chin's.

King.

Borders down

1.

ϕ [Door ~~flat, L.~~ – Door, 2E. L. – before which, hangs a piece of tapestry. – A heavy, antique table and chair disc.d on ty. R.E. – in front. – Door in R.H. locked, and key in lock.]

[Hubert. [Act.] [B Paper, No 1. – and Blinding irons.]
2 Attendants.
Arthur. [Bow and arrows.]
See Pan of imit.n fire, ready, L.]

[Going L. – stops, – then speaks.]

⊙ [Hubert unlocks D R. and calls.]

ϕ [Hub. goes to chair, R. – sits, – and leans on table.]

For England go; I will whet on the king.

Lew. Strong reasons make strong actions: Let us go;

If you say, ay, the king will not say, no. [*Exeunt*, L. E. – thro' tent.]

ACT IV.

1.

SCENE I. Northampton.[2] *A Room in the Castle.* [2 Gr.] ϕ

Enter HUBERT *and Two* Attendants. [L. Door 2E.]

Hub. Heat me these irons hot; and, look thou stand [gives the irons to 2nd Att.t]

Within the arras: when I strike my foot

Upon the bosom of the ground, rush forth:

And bind the boy, which you shall find with me,

Fast to the chair: be heedful: hence, and watch.

1 *Attend.* I hope, your warrant will bear out the deed.

Hub. Uncleanly scruples! Fear not you: look to't.— [*Exeunt* Attendants, L. 2E.] ⊙

Young lad, come forth; I have to say with you.

Enter ARTHUR. [door R.H. 2 E.]

Arth. Good morrow, Hubert.

Hub. Good morrow, little prince. ϕ

² *Northampton.*] The fact is, that Arthur was first confined at Falaise, and afterwards at Rouen, in Normandy, where he was put to death.—Our author has deviated, in this particular, from the history, and brought king John's nephew to England; but there is no circumstance, either in the original play, or in this of Shakspeare, to point out the particular castle in which he is supposed to be confined. The castle of Northampton has been mentioned, in some modern editions, as the place, merely because, in the first Act, King John *seems* to have been in that town. In the old copy there is no where any notice of place.

Arth. As little prince (having so great a title
To be more prince,) as may be.—You are sad.
Hub. Indeed, I have been merrier.
Arth. Mercy on me!
Methinks, no body should be sad but I:
Yet, I remember, when I was in France,
Young gentlemen would be as sad as night,
Only for wantonness. By my christendom,
So I were out of prison, and kept sheep,
I should be as merry as the day is long;
And so I would be here, but that I doubt
My uncle practises more harm to me: /Pause./
He is afraid of me, and I of him:
Is it my fault that I was Geffrey's son?
No, indeed, is't not; And I would to heaven,
I were your son, so you would love me, Hubert.
Hub. If I talk to him, with his innocent prate
He will awake my mercy, which lies dead:
Therefore I will be sudden, and despatch. [*Aside.*
Arth. Are you sick, Hubert? you look pale to-day:
In sooth, I would you were a little sick;
That I might sit all night, and watch with you:
I warrant, I love you more than you do me.
Hub. His words do take possession of my bosom.—
Read here, young Arthur. [*Showing a paper.*] How now, foolish rheum! [*Aside.*
~~Turning dispiteous torture out of door!~~
I must be brief; lest resolution drop
Out at mine eyes, in tender womanish tears.——
Can you not read it? is it not fair writ?
Arth. Too fairly, Hubert, for so foul effect:
Must you with hot irons burn out both mine eyes?
Hub. Young boy, I must.
Arth. And will you?
Hub. And I will.

/Arth; - who has been playing with his bow, on L, - suddenly turns observes Hubert, intently, and goes to him./ drops Bow c[illegible]

sitting on Stool L of Chair

2.

rises gets on stool, and lays his head on Hubert's shoulder.

2 Attendants.
/piece of rope - the blinding irons, ~~red-hot~~ - and pan of fire./

/~~Rises, and paces a few steps~~ Hubert in agitation, ~~then~~ gives him the warrant, - on seeing Arthur's emotion, he turns away./

drops warrant/.

Arth. Have you the heart? When your head did but ake,
I knit my handkerchief about your brows,
(The best I had, a princess wrought it me,)
And I did never ask it you again:
And with my hand at midnight held your head;
And, like the watchful minutes to the hour,
Still and anon cheer'd up the heavy time;
Saying, What lack you? and, Where lies your grief?
Or, What good love may I perform for you?
Many a poor man's son would have lain still,
And ne'er have spoke a loving word to you;
But you at your sick service had a prince.
Nay, you may think, my love was crafty love,
And call it, cunning; Do, an if you will:
If heaven be pleas'd that you must use me ill,
Why, then you must.—Will you put out mine eyes?
These eyes, that never did, nor never shall,
So much as frown on you?

Hub. I have sworn to do it;
And with hot irons must I burn them out.

Arth. Ah, none, but in this iron age, would do it!
The iron of itself, though heat red-hot,
Approaching near these eyes, would drink my tears,
And quench his fiery indignation,
Even in the matter of mine innocence:
Nay, after that, consume away in rust,
But for containing fire to harm mine eye.
Are you more stubborn-hard than hammer'd iron?
An if an angel should have come to me,
And told me, Hubert should put out mine eyes,
I would not have believ'd no tongue, but Hubert's.

Hub. Come forth. [*Stamps.*

3.

Re-enter Attendants, *with Cord, Irons,* &c. /L.D./

Do as I bid you do.

Arth. O, save me, Hubert, save me! my eyes are out,
Even with the fierce looks of these bloody men.

Hub. Give me the iron, I say, and bind him here.

Arth. Alas, what need you be so boist'rous-rough?
I will not struggle, I will stand stone-still.
For heaven's sake, Hubert, let me not be bound!
Nay, hear me, Hubert! drive these men away,
And I will sit as quiet as a lamb;
I will not stir, nor wince, nor speak a word,
Nor look upon the iron angerly:
Thrust but these men away, and I'll forgive you,
Whatever torment you do put me to.

Hub. Go, stand within; let me alone with him.

1 *Attend.* I am best pleas'd to be from such a deed. [*Exeunt* Attendants, L.D./

Arth. Alas! I then have chid away my friend;
He hath a stern look, but a gentle heart:—
Let him come back, that his compassion may
Give life to yours.

Hub. Come, boy, prepare yourself.

/weeping bitterly./ *Arth.* Oh! Oh! Is there no remedy?

Hub. None, but to lose your eyes.

Arth. O heaven!—that there were but a mote in yours,
A grain, a dust, a gnat, a wand'ring hair,
Any annoyance in that precious sense!
Then, feeling what small things are boist'rous there,
Your vile intent must needs seem horrible.

Hub. Is this your promise? go to, hold your tongue.

Arth. ~~Hubert, the utterance of a brace of tongues~~

§

/Arthur runs, shrieking, to cling round Hubert, R. – The 2nd Attend^t puts down the pan of fire, and gives the iron across to Hub^t, as he commands, – 1st Attend^t has the rope, and seizes Arthur, – they both strive to disengage his arms and legs from Hub^t, during his speech, and drag him away, to L – as he says, – "Nay, hear me, Hubert," &c./

3.

King John.
Salisbury.
Essex.
Pembroke.
Norfolk.
Fitzwalter.
~~De Warrenne~~.
Arundel.
Oxford.
Percy.
De Clare.
Hereford.
De Ros.
1st English Knights.
1. D^o Heralds.

Flourish ready. R.

~~Must needs want pleading for a pair of eyes:~~
Let me not hold my tongue; let me not, Hubert! /Kneels/
Or, Hubert, if you will, cut out my tongue,
So I may keep mine eyes; O, spare mine eyes;
Though to no use, but still to look on you! /starts up/.
Lo, by my troth, the instrument is cold, /
And would not harm me.

Hub. I can heat it, boy.

Arth. No, in good sooth; the fire is dead with grief, /goes up to fire/
Being create for comfort, to be us'd
In undeserv'd extremes: See else yourself;
There is no malice in this burning coal;
The breath of heaven hath blown his spirit out,
And strew'd repentant ashes on his head.

Hub. But with my breath I can revive it, boy.

Arth. And if you do, you will but make it blush, /down LH/
And glow with shame of your proceedings, Hubert: /pause./
Nay, it, perchance, will sparkle in your eyes;
And, like a dog that is compell'd to fight,
Snatch at his master that doth tarre him on.[3]
All things, that you should use to do me wrong,
Deny their office: only you do lack
That mercy, which fierce fire, and iron, extends,
Creatures of note, for mercy-lacking uses.

Ø *Hub.* Well, see to live; I will not touch thine eyes
For all the treasure that thine uncle owes: /Kneeling/.
Yet am I sworn, and I did purpose, boy,
With this same very iron to burn them out.

Arth. O, now you look like Hubert! all this while
You were disguised.

Hub. Φ Peace: no more. ~~Adieu;~~

Ø /throws away the irons, - kneels - and embraces Arthur./

Φ /~~goes to LD, listens, and returns~~./

[3] —— tarre *him on.*] i. e. stimulate, set him on. Supposed to be derived from ταράσσω, excito.

Your uncle must not know but you are dead:
I'll fill these dogged spies with false reports.
And, pretty child, sleep doubtless, and secure,
That Hubert, for the wealth of all the world,
Will not offend thee.

Arth. O heaven!—I thank you, Hubert,

Hub. Silence; no more: Go closely in with me.[4]
Much danger do I undergo for thee. [*Exeunt.*

SCENE II.

The same. A Room of State in the Palace.

Enter KING JOHN, *crowned;* PEMBROKE, SALISBURY, *and other Lords. The King takes his State.*

K. John. Here once again we sit, once again crown'd,
And look'd upon, I hope, with cheerful eyes.

Pem. This once again, but that your highness pleas'd,
Was once superfluous: you were crown'd before,
And that high royalty was ne'er pluck'd off;
The faiths of men ne'er stained with revolt;
Fresh expectation troubled not the land,
With any long'd-for change, or better state.

Sal. Therefore, to be possess'd with double pomp,
To guard[5] a title that was rich before,
To gild refined gold, to paint the lily,
To throw a perfume on the violet,
To smooth the ice, or add another hue
Unto the rainbow, or with taper-light

[4] —— Go closely *in with me.*] i. e. secretly, privately.
[5] *To guard* —] i. e. to *fringe,* or *lace.*

To seek the beauteous eye of heaven to garnish,
Is wasteful, and ridiculous excess.

Pem. But that your royal pleasure must be done,
This act is as an ancient tale new told;
And, in the last repeating, troublesome,
Being urged at a time unseasonable.

Sal. In this, the antique and well-noted face
Of plain old form is much disfigured:
And, like a shifted wind unto a sail,
It makes the course of thoughts to fetch about;
Startles and frights consideration;
Makes sound opinion sick, and truth suspected,
For putting on so new a fashion'd robe.

Pem. When workmen strive to do better than well,
They do confound their skill in covetousness:[6]
And, oftentimes, excusing of a fault,
Doth make the fault the worse by the excuse;
As patches, set upon a little breach,
Discredit more in hiding of the fault,
Than did the fault before it was so patch'd.

Bigot. *Sal.* To this effect, before you were new-crown'd, /B./
We breath'd our counsel: but it pleas'd your highness
To overbear it; and we are all well pleas'd;
Since all and every part of what we would,
Doth make a stand at what your highness will.

K. John. Some reasons of this double coronation
I have possess'd you with, and think them strong;
And more, more strong, (when lesser is my fear,)
I shall indue you with: Mean time, but ask
What you would have reform'd, that is not well;
And well shall you perceive, how willingly
I will both hear and grant you your requests.

[6] *They do confound their skill in* covetousness:] i. e. not by their avarice, but in an eager emulation, an intense desire of excelling.

Pem. Then I, (as one that am the tongue of these,
To sound the purposes[7] of all their hearts,)
Both for myself and them, (but, chief of all,
Your safety, for the which myself and them
Bend their best studies,) heartily request
The enfranchisement of Arthur; whose restraint
Doth move the murmuring lips of discontent
To break into this dangerous argument,—
If, what in rest you have, in right you hold,
Why then your fears, (which, as they say, attend
The steps of wrong,) should move you to mew up
Your tender kinsman, and to choke his days
With barbarous ignorance, and deny his youth
The rich advantage of good exercise?[8]
That the time's enemies may not have this
To grace occasions, let it be our suit,
That you have bid us ask his liberty;
Which for our goods we do no further ask,
Than whereupon our weal, on you depending,
Counts it your weal, he have his liberty.

K. John. Let it be so; I do commit his youth

Enter Hubert.

To your direction.—Hubert, what news with you?

Salis. ~~*Pem.*~~ This is the man should do the bloody deed;
He show'd his warrant to a friend of mine:
The image of a wicked heinous fault
Lives in his eye; that close aspect of his

[7] *To sound the purposes*—] To *declare*, to *publish* the desires of all those.

[8] —— *good exercise?*] In the middle ages, the whole education of princes and noble youths consisted in martial exercises, &c. These could not be easily had in a prison, where mental improvements might have been afforded as well as any where else; but this sort of education never entered into the thoughts of our active, warlike, but illiterate nobility. Percy.

/The Lords appear to second Pembroke's request./

/John rises, as to break up the assembly, — All bow. Lords, K. — to Lords — Hubert Enter, L. — and speaks to the King, as he descends from the Dais./

Bastard.
Peter of Pomfret.
2 Attendants.

Ø /The Lords start, - and appear much excited./

Does show the mood of a much-troubled breast;
And I do fearfully believe, 'tis done,
What we so fear'd he had a charge to do.
Pem. ~~Sal.~~ The colour of the king doth come and go,
Between his purpose and his conscience,
~~Like heralds 'twixt two dreadful battles set:~~
His passion is so ripe, it needs must break.
Pem. And, when it breaks, I fear, will issue thence
The foul corruption of a sweet child's death.
K. John. We cannot hold mortality's strong hand:— /to Hubert./ who goes up R.H.
Good lords, although my will to give is living, /adv'g to them./
The suit which you demand is gone and dead: Ø
He tells us, Arthur is deceas'd to-night.
Sal. Indeed, we fear'd, his sickness was past cure.
Pem. Indeed, we heard how near his death he was,
Before the child himself felt he was sick:
This must be answer'd, either here, or hence.
K. John. Why do you bend such solemn brows on me?
Think you, I bear the shears of destiny?
Have I commandment on the pulse of life?
Sal. It is apparent foul-play; and 'tis shame,
That greatness should so grossly offer it:
So thrive it in your game! and so farewell. /going L.H.2 E.
Pem. Stay yet, lord Salisbury; we'll go with thee, / All go up. R./
~~And find the inheritance of this poor child,~~
His little kingdom of a forced grave.
That blood, which ow'd the breath of all this isle,
Three foot of it doth hold; Bad world the while!
This must not be thus borne: this will break out
To all our sorrows, and ere long, I doubt.
[*Exeunt* Lords, L.2E. in violent agitation./
K. John. They burn in indignation; I repent;
There is no sure foundation set on blood;
No certain life achiev'd by others' death.——

*

Enter a ~~*Messenger*~~ Knight. hastily, down R. - kneels.

A fearful eye thou hast; Where is that blood,
That I have seen inhabit in those cheeks?
~~So foul a sky clears not without a storm:~~
~~Pour down thy weather:~~—How goes all in France?
Mess. From France to England.—Never such a power, /rises./
For any foreign preparation,
Was levied in the body of a land!
The copy of your speed is learn'd by them;
For, when you should be told they do prepare,
The tidings come, that they are all arriv'd.
K. John. O, where hath our intelligence been drunk?
Where hath it slept? Where is my mother's care?
That such an army could be drawn in France,
And she not hear of it?
Mess. My liege, her ear
Is stopp'd with dust; the first of April, died
Your noble mother: And, as I hear, my lord,
The lady Constance in a frenzy died
Three days before: ~~but this from rumour's tongue~~
~~I idly heard; if true, or false, I know not.~~
K. John. Withhold thy speed, dreadful occasion!
O, make a league with me, till I have pleas'd
My discontented peers!—What! mother dead?
How wildly then walks my estate in France![9]—
Under whose conduct came those powers of France,
That thou for truth giv'st out, are landed here?
Mess. Under the Dauphin.

[9] *How wildly then walks my estate in France!*] i. e. how ill my affairs go in France!—The verb, to *walk*, is used with great license by old writers.

∅ /The Bastard goes down, L. – Hubert is on the R./ R at Back

Enter the Bastard *and* PETER *of* POMFRET. with Two Attendants /LL./ ∅

K. John. /~ Thou hast made me giddy
With these ill tidings.—Now, what says the world
To your proceedings? do not seek to stuff
My head with more ill news, for it is full.

/L./ *Bast.* But, if you be afeard to hear the worst,
Then let the worst, unheard, fall on your head.

K. John. Bear with me, cousin; for I was amaz'd[1]
Under the tide: but now I breathe again
Aloft the flood; and can give audience
To any tongue, speak it of what it will.

Bast. How I have sped among the clergymen,
The sums I have collected shall express.
But, as I travelled hither through the land,
I find the people strangely fantasied;
Possess'd with rumours, full of idle dreams;
Not knowing what they fear, but full of fear:
And here's a prophet,[2] that I brought with me
From forth the streets of Pomfret, whom I found
With many hundreds treading on his heels;
To whom he sung, in rude harsh-sounding rhymes,
That, ere the next Ascension-day at noon,
Your highness should deliver up your crown.

K. John. Thou idle dreamer, wherefore didst thou so?

Peter. Foreknowing that the truth will fall out so. /at back, L./

K. John. Hubert, away with him; imprison him;
And on that day at noon, whereon, he says,

[1] —— *I was* amaz'd —] i. e. stunned, confounded.

[2] *And here's a prophet,*] This man was a hermit in great repute with the common people. Notwithstanding the event is said to have fallen out as he had prophesied, the poor fellow was inhumanly dragged at horses' tails through the streets of Warham, and, together with his son, who appears to have been even more innocent than his father, hanged afterwards upon a gibbet. See Holinshed's *Chronicle*, under the year 1213.

put to death:
I ~~shall~~ yield ~~up~~ my crown, let him be ~~hang'd~~:
Deliver him to safety,[3] and return,
For I must use thee.—O my gentle cousin,
and Att.ᵗ [Exit HUBERT, with PETER, } |L.l.|
Hear'st thou the news abroad, who are arriv'd?

Bast. The French, my lord; men's mouths are full of it:
Besides, I met lord Bigot, and lord Salisbury,
(With eyes as red as new-enkindled fire,)
And others more, going to seek the grave
Of Arthur, who, they say, is kill'd to-night
On your suggestion.

K. John. Gentle kinsman, go,
And thrust thyself into their companies:
I have a way to win their loves again;
Bring them before me.

Bast. I will seek them out.

K. John. Nay, but make haste; the better foot before.——
O, let me have no subject enemies,
When adverse foreigners affright my towns
With dreadful pomp of stout invasion!—
Be Mercury, set feathers to thy heels;
And fly, like thought, from them to me again.

Bast. The spirit of the time shall teach me speed.
[*Exit*, ~~R.~~/

K. John. ~~Spoke like a spriteful noble gentleman.~~—
/to Knight./ Go after him; for he, perhaps, shall need
Some messenger betwixt me and the peers;
And be thou he.

~~*Mess.* With all my heart, my liege.~~
[*Exit*, Knt. ~~R.~~/

K. John. My mother dead!

[3] *Deliver him to safety,*] That is, *Give him into safe custody.*

LH.2.E. behind K.J.

LH2E followed by Herald

Re-enter HUBERT.

Hub. My lord, they say, five moons were seen to-night:[4]
Four fixed; and the fifth did whirl about
The other four, in wond'rous motion.
K. John. Five moons?
Hub. Old men, and beldams, in the streets
Do prophecy upon it dangerously:
Young Arthur's death is common in their mouths:
And when they talk of him, they shake their heads,
And whisper one another in the ear;
And he, that speaks, doth gripe the hearer's wrist;
Whilst he, that hears, makes fearful action,
With wrinkled brows, with nods, with rolling eyes.
I saw a smith stand with his hammer, thus,
The whilst his iron did on the anvil cool,
With open mouth swallowing a tailor's news;
Who, with his shears and measure in his hand,
Standing on slippers, (which his nimble haste
Had falsely thrust upon contrary feet,)[5]

[4] —— *five moons were seen to-night:* &c.] This incident is mentioned by few of our historians. I have met with it no where but in Matthew of Westminster and Polydore Virgil, with a small alteration. These kind of appearances were more common about that time than either before or since. GREY.

[5] —— *slippers, (which his nimble haste*
Had falsely thrust upon contrary *feet,)*] Dr. Johnson says, "I know not how the commentators understand this important passage, which, in Dr. Warburton's edition, is marked as eminently beautiful, and, on the whole, not without justice. But Shakspeare seems to have confounded the man's shoes with his gloves. He that is frighted or hurried may put his hand into the wrong glove, but either shoe will equally admit either foot. The author seems to be disturbed by the disorder which he describes." But Dr. Johnson forgets that ancient *slippers* might possibly be very different from modern ones, and the commentators have produced many passages to prove the shoe, boot, &c. were right and left legged.

Told of a many thousand warlike French,
That were embatteled and rank'd in Kent:
Another lean unwash'd artificer
Cuts off his tale, and talks of Arthur's death.
K. John. Why seek'st thou to possess me with these fears?
Why urgest thou so oft young Arthur's death?
Thy hand hath murder'd him: I had mighty cause
To wish him dead, but thou hadst none to kill him.
Hub. Had none, my lord! why, did you not provoke me?
K. John. It is the curse of kings,[6] to be attended
By slaves, that take their humours for a warrant
To break within the bloody house of life:
And, on the winking of authority,
To understand a law; to know the meaning
Of dangerous majesty, when, perchance, it frowns
More upon humour than advis'd respect.[7]
Hub. Here is your hand and seal for what I did.
K. John. O, when the last account 'twixt heaven and earth
Is to be made, then shall this hand and seal
Witness against us to damnation!
How oft the sight of means to do ill deeds,
Makes deeds ill done! Hadest not thou been by,
A fellow by the hand of nature mark'd,
Quoted,[8] and sign'd, to do a deed of shame,
This murder had not come into my mind:
But, taking note of thy abhorr'd aspéct,
Finding thee fit for bloody villainy,
~~Apt, liable, to be employ'd in danger,~~
I faintly broke with thee of Arthur's death;
And thou, to be endeared to a king,

[6] *It is the curse of kings,* &c.] This plainly hints at Davison's case, in the affair of Mary Queen of Scots.

[7] —— *advis'd* respect.] i. e. deliberate consideration.

[8] *Quoted,*] i. e. observed, distinguished.

Made it no conscience to destroy a prince.
Hub. My lord,——
K. John. Hadst thou but shook thy head,[9] or made a pause,
When I spake darkly what I purposed;
Or turn'd an eye of doubt upon my face,
And bid me tell my tale in express words;
Deep shame had struck me dumb, made me break off,
And those thy fears might have wrought fears in me:
But thou didst understand me by my signs,
And didst in signs again parley with sin;
Yea, without stop, didst let thy heart consent,
And, consequently, thy rude hand to act
The deed, which both our tongues held vile to name.—
Out of my sight, and never see me more!
My nobles leave me; and my state is brav'd,
Even at my gates, with ranks of foreign powers:
Nay, in the body of this fleshly land,
This kingdom, this confine of blood and breath,
Hostility and civil tumult reigns
Between my conscience, and my cousin's death.
Hub. Arm you against your other enemies,

[9] *Hadst thou but shook thy head,* &c.] There are many touches of nature in this conference of John with Hubert. A man engaged in wickedness would keep the profit to himself, and transfer the guilt to his accomplice. These reproaches, vented against Hubert, are not the words of art or policy, but the eruptions of a mind swelling with a consciousness of a crime, and desirous of discharging its misery on another.

This account of the timidity of guilt is drawn *ab ipsis recessibus mentis,* from the intimate knowledge of mankind, particularly that line in which he says, that *to have bid him tell his tale* in *express* words, would have *struck him dumb;* nothing is more certain than that bad men use all the arts of fallacy upon themselves, palliate their actions to their own minds by gentle terms, and hide themselves from their own detection in ambiguities and subterfuges.

I'll make a peace between your soul and you.
~~Young Arthur is alive:~~ This hand of mine
Is yet a maiden and an innocent hand,
Not painted with the crimson spots of blood.
Within this bosom never enter'd yet
The dreadful motion of a murd'rous thought,[1]
And you have slander'd nature in my form;
Which, howsoever rude exteriorly,
Is yet the cover of a fairer mind
Than to be butcher of an innocent child. o → Young Arthur is alive.

K. John. Doth Arthur live? O, haste thee to the peers,
Throw this report on their incensed rage,
And make them tame to their obedience!
Forgive the comment that my passion made
Upon thy feature; for my rage was blind,
And foul imaginary eyes of blood
Presented thee more hideous than thou art.
O, answer not; but to my closet bring
The angry lords, with all expedient haste:
~~I conjure thee but slowly; run more fast.~~ [*Exeunt.*
John, [illegible]. Hub [illegible]

SCENE III.

The same. Before the Castle. / Set to [illegible] /

Enter ARTHUR, *on the Walls,* / [illegible] / ⌀

Arth. The wall is high; and yet will I leap down:—
Good ground, be pitiful, and hurt me not!—

[1] *The dreadful motion of a* murd'rous *thought,*] Nothing can be falser than what Hubert here says in his own vindication; for we find, from a preceding scene, *the motion of a murd'rous thought had entered into him;* and that very deeply; and it was with difficulty that the tears, the entreaties, and the innocence of Arthur had diverted and suppressed it. WARBURTON.

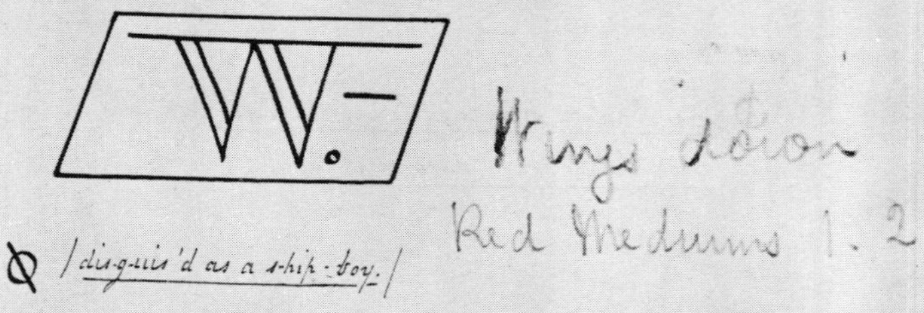

⌀ / disguis'd as a ship-boy. /

Φ /into the round tower, - rolls thro' the entrance arch, and down the steps, R. on to the stage./

Φ /Salisbury has an open letter, in his hand, - the Lords crowd round him, as they enter./

Φ /The Bastard speaks as he enters, - Lords turn, and, by their movement, leave Salisbury in advance of them./

There's few, or none, do know me; if they did,
This ship-boy's semblance hath disguis'd me quite.
I am afraid; and yet I'll venture it.
If I get down, and do not break my limbs,
I'll find a thousand shifts to get away:
As good to die, and go, as die, and stay.
[*Leaps down.* Φ
O me! my uncle's spirit is in these stones:—
Heaven take my soul, and England keep my bones!
[*Dies.*

Fitzwalter, - ~~De Warenne~~, - Arundel,
Enter PEMBROKE, SALISBURY, *and* BIGOT. /R. 2 l. e./ Φ

Sal. Lords, I will meet him at saint Edmund's-Bury;
It is our safety, and we must embrace
This gentle offer of the perilous time.
1st R. *Pem.* Who brought that letter from the cardinal?
Sal. The count Melun, a noble lord of France;
Whose private with me,[2] of the Dauphin's love,
Is much more general than these lines import.
R. *Big.* To-morrow morning let us meet him then.
Sal. Or, rather then set forward: for 'twill be
Two long days' journey, lords, or e'er we meet. /All going, R./

Enter the Bastard. /L. 2 l. e./ Φ

Bast. Once more to-day well met, distemper'd[3] lords! /down L./
The king, by me, requests your presence straight.
Sal. The king hath dispossess'd himself of us;
We will not line his thin bestained cloak
With our pure honours, nor attend the foot
That leaves the print of blood where-e'er it walks:
Return, and tell him so; we know the worst.

[2] *Whose private,* &c.] i. e. whose private account of the Dauphin's affection to our cause is much more ample than the letters.
[3] —— *distemper'd*—] i. e. ruffled, out of humour.

Bast. Whate'er you think, good words, I think, were best.

Sal. Our griefs, and not our manners, reason now.[4]

Bast. But there is little reason in your grief;
Therefore, 'twere reason, you had manners now.

Pem. Sir, sir, impatience hath his privilege.

Bast. 'Tis true; to hurt his master, no man else.

Sal. This is the prison: What is he lies here?
[*Seeing* ARTHUR.

Pem. O death, made proud with pure and princely beauty!
The earth had not a hole to hide this deed.

Sal. Murder, as hating what himself hath done,
Doth lay it open, to urge on revenge.

Big. Or, when he doom'd this beauty to a grave,
Found it too precious-princely for a grave.

Sal. Sir Richard, what think you? Have you beheld,
Or have you read, or heard? or could you think?
Or do you almost think, although you see,
That you do see? could thought, without this object,
Form such another? This is the very top,
The height, the crest, or crest unto the crest,
Of murder's arms: this is the bloodiest shame,
The wildest savag'ry, the vilest stroke,
That ever wall-ey'd wrath, or staring rage,
Presented to the tears of soft remorse.

Pemb. All murders past do stand excus'd in this:
And this, so sole, and so unmatchable,
Shall give a holiness, a purity,
To the yet-unbegotten sin of time;
And prove a deadly bloodshed but a jest,
Exampled by this heinous spectacle.

[4] —— reason *now*.] To *reason*, in Shakspeare, is not so often to *argue*, as to *talk*.

/ Going up towards Castle, – seeing the body of Arth', – starts, and stoops to raise it and examine the face, – upon his exclamation, the Lords rush up, and crowd around it, – the Bastard, also, goes a few paces up stage. /

ϕ / head - not - hand - in allusion to the circle of rays which surrounds the heads of saints, in pictures. /

R. M. B.

Bast. It is a damned and a bloody work;
The graceless action of a heavy hand,
If that it be the work of any hand.
Sal. If that it be the work of any hand?—
~~We had a kind of light, what would ensue:~~
It is the shameful work of Hubert's hand;
The practice, and the purpose, of the king:— / Kneeling /
From whose obedience I forbid my soul,
Kneeling before this ruin of sweet life,
And breathing to his breathless excellence
The incense of a vow, a holy vow;
Never to taste the pleasures of the world,[5]
Never to be infected with delight,
Nor conversant with ease and idleness,
Till I have set a glory to this ~~hand~~, head, ϕ
By giving it the worship of revenge.
Pem. ~~Big.~~ Our souls religiously confirm thy words.

Enter HUBERT. / R. U. E. /

Hub. Lords, I am hot with haste in seeking you: / down, R /
Arthur doth live; the king hath sent for you.
Sal. ~~O, he is bold, and blushes not at death~~:—
Avaunt, thou hateful villain, get thee gone!
Hub. I am no villain.
Sal. / R. C. / Must I rob the law?
[*Drawing his sword.*
/ C. / *Bast.* Your sword is bright, sir; put it up again.
Sal. Not till I sheath it in a murderer's skin.
/ L / *Hub.* Stand back, lord Salisbury, stand back, I say;
By heaven, I think, my sword's as sharp as yours:
I would not have you, lord, forget yourself,

[5] —— *a holy vow;*
Never to taste the pleasures of the world,] This is a copy of the vows made in the ages of superstition and chivalry.

Nor tempt the danger of my true defence;[5]
Lest I, by marking of your rage, forget
Your worth, your greatness, and nobility.
Big. Out, dunghill! dar'st thou brave a nobleman?
Hub. Not for my life: but yet I dare defend
My innocent life against an emperor.
Sal. Thou art a murderer.
Hub. Do not prove me so;
Yet, I am none:[6] Whose tongue soe'er speaks false,
Not truly speaks; who speaks not truly, lies.
Pemb. Cut him to pieces.
Bast. Keep the peace, I say.
Sal. Stand by, or I shall gall you, Faulconbridge.
Bast. Thou wert better gall the devil, Salisbury:
If thou but frown on me, or stir thy foot,
Or teach thy hasty spleen to do me shame,
I'll strike thee dead. Put up thy sword betime;
Or I'll so maul you and your toasting-iron,
That you shall think the devil is come from hell.
Big. What wilt thou do, renowned Faulconbridge?
Second a villain, and a murderer?
Hub. Lord Bigot, I am none.
Big. Who kill'd this prince!
Hub. 'Tis not an hour since I left him well:
I honour'd him, I lov'd him; and will weep
My date of life out, for his sweet life's loss.
Sal. Trust not those cunning waters of his eyes,
For villainy is not without such rheum;
And he, long traded in it, makes it seem
Like rivers of remorse[7] and innocency.

[5] —— *true defence;*] *Honest* defence; defence in a *good cause.*

[6] *Do not prove me so;*
Yet, *I am none:*] Do not make me a murderer, by compelling me to kill you; I am *hitherto* not a murderer.

[7] *Like rivers of* remorse—] *Remorse* here, as almost every where in these plays, and the contemporary books, signifies *pity.*

/All draw, and advance to Hub./

/Hub rushes up to the body./ Sal xes to L.C.

Face go up

/Hub' X's up to Arthur's body, and is engaged, with expressions of deep grief, in raising it./

Away, with me, all you whose souls abhor
The uncleanly savours of a slaughter-house;
For I am stifled with this smell of sin.
Big. Away, toward Bury, to the Dauphin there!
Pem. There, tell the king, he may inquire us out.
[*Exeunt* Lords.
Bast. Here's a good world!—Knew you of this fair work?
Beyond the infinite and boundless reach
Of mercy, if thou didst this deed of death,
Art thou damn'd, Hubert.
Hub. Do but hear me, sir.
Bast. Ha! I'll tell thee what;
Thou art damn'd as black—nay, nothing is so black;
Thou art more deep damn'd than prince Lucifer:
There is not yet so ugly a fiend of hell
As thou shalt be, if thou didst kill this child.
Hub. Upon my soul,—
Bast. If thou didst but consent
To this most cruel act, do but despair,
And, if thou want'st a cord, the smallest thread
That ever spider twisted from her womb
Will serve to strangle thee; a rush will be
A beam to hang thee on; or would'st thou drown thyself,
Put but a little water in a spoon,
And it shall be as all the ocean,
Enough to stifle such a villain up.——
I do suspect thee very grievously.
Hub. If I in act, consent, or sin of thought
Be guilty of the stealing that sweet breath
Which was embounded in this beauteous clay,
Let hell want pains enough to torture me!
I left him well.
Bast. Go, bear him in thine arms.—
I am amaz'd,[8] methinks; and lose my way

[8] *I am* amaz'd,] i. e. *confounded.*

Among the thorns and dangers of this world.—
How easy dost thou take all England up!
From forth this morsel of dead royalty,
The life, the right, and truth of all this realm
Is fled to heaven; and England now is left
To tug and scamble,[9] and to part by the teeth
The unowed interest[1] of proud-swelling state.
Now, for the bare-pick'd bone of majesty,
Doth dogged war bristle his angry crest,
And snarleth in the gentle eyes of peace:
Now powers from home, and discontents at home, × L.H.
Meet in one line; and vast confusion waits
(As doth a raven on a sick-fallen beast,)
The imminent decay of wrested pomp.[2]
Now happy he, whose cloak and cincture can
Hold out this tempest. Bear away that child, × R.H.
And follow me with speed; I'll to the king:
A thousand businesses are brief in hand,
And heaven itself doth frown upon the land.

[*Exeunt*, R.U.E.]

ACT V.

SCENE I. The same. ~~A Room in the Palace.~~ The Temple Church. [2d Gr.]

~~Enter~~ *King* JOHN, PANDULPH *with the Crown,* ~~and~~ *Attendants, &c. &c. disc.d*

K. John. Thus have I yielded up into your hand
The circle of my glory. [rises.]

[9] *To tug and* scamble,] *Scamble* and *scramble* have the same meaning.
[1] *The* unowed *interest*—] i. e. the interest which has no proper owner to claim it.
[2] *The imminent decay of* wrested pomp.] i. e. *greatness obtained by violence;* or rather, greatness wrested from its possessor.

See Organ ready. L.

Kneels kisses his hand.

Time Min's.

Organ Music, L. [as the Drop rises.]

[K John is in the act of giving his crown, to Pand.—who places it on a cushion, held by a Priest, on R.—K John—kneeling—then places his hands between those of Pandulph, as doing homage.—Organ ceases.]

King John.
Hubert. [cushion]
Pandulph [2d]
Essex.
4 Eng. Knights
Hereford.
Oxford.
Grand Master
4 Knts Templar
2 Do Hospitallers
2 Ord. Abbots.
4 Banners
6 Monks.
2 Gentlemen.
6 Bishops.
Archbishop.
Notar' Apost.
2 Eng. Heralds.
Priest [Cross]
Bastard.

Priest w Temple Ban'. – Priest, w Host Ban'. Knt – Knt. Priest w Trinity Ban'. – Priest w Temp Ban.

Monk. Monk. Monk. Monk. Bishop. Gent'. Gent'.

Bishop. Bishop. Bishop. Bishop. Bishop. Bishop. Bishop.

M'd Abbot. M'd Abbot.

Knt Hospit'. Knt Hospit'. Archbishop. Notarius Apostolicus. Herald.

Knt Temp'. Knt Temp'. Knt Temp'. Knt Temp'. Knt Temp'. Knt Temp'. Hereford. Hubert. Oxford. K John. Pandulph. Herald. Priest. Knt Temp'. Knt Temp'. Essex.

Grand Master of Templars.

R. (Disposition, as Act 5, – com'.) L.

Φ / Rises, and X'es with his Suite, to R. /

Φ / with all, except Essex, Oxford, Hereford, – the 2 Knights, and 2 Heralds, – the Gent'n of his Suite, take up the bags of money, – place them on cushions, and carry them off. /

Lewis / Bohst. No 2. / Melun. De Neuville. De Bretel. De Roye. De Beaumont. Salisbury. Pembroke. Norfolk. Fitzwalter. Arundel. De Roi. De Blair. 2 Heralds.

2.

Pand. Take again
[*Giving* JOHN *the Crown,* – John gives it to Hub. on his R. – who receives it on a cushion, and gives it to M'd Abbot, up R.C. /
From this my hand, as holding of the pope,
Your sovereign greatness and authority.

K. John. Now keep your holy word: go meet the French;
And from his holiness use all your power
To stop their marches, 'fore we are inflam'd.
Our discontented counties do revolt;
Our people quarrel with obedience;
Swearing allegiance, and the love of soul,
To stranger blood, to foreign royalty.
This inundation of mistemper'd humour
Rests by you only to be qualified.
Then pause not; for the present time's so sick,
That present medicine must be minister'd,
Or overthrow incurable ensues.

2.

Pand. It was my breath that blew this tempest up, Φ
Upon your stubborn usage of the pope:
But, since you are a gentle convertite,[3]
My tongue shall hush again this storm of war,
And make fair weather in your blustering land.
On this Ascension-day, remember well,
Upon your oath of service to the pope,
Go I to make the French lay down their arms.
[*Exit,* R. – / Φ

K. John. Is this Ascension-day? Did not the prophet
Say, that, before Ascension-day at noon,
My crown I should give off? Even so I have:
I did suppose, it should be on constraint;
But, heaven be thank'd, it is but voluntary.

[3] —— *a gentle* convertite,] A *convertite* is a *convert.*

Enter the Bastard. /R./

Bast. All Kent hath yielded; nothing there holds out,
But Dover castle: London hath receiv'd,
Like a kind host, the Dauphin and his powers:
Your nobles will not hear you, but are gone
To offer service to your enemy;
And wild amazement hurries up and down
The little number of your doubtful friends.
K. John. Would not my lords return to me again,
After they heard young Arthur was alive?
Bast. They found him dead, and cast into the streets;
An empty casket, where the jewel of life
By some damn'd hand was robb'd and ta'en away.
K. John. That villain Hubert told me, he did live.
Bast. So, on my soul, he did, for aught he knew.
But wherefore do you droop? why look you sad?
Be great in act, as you have been in thought;
Let not the world see fear, and sad distrust,
Govern the motion of a kingly eye:
Be stirring as the time; be fire with fire;
Threaten the threat'ner, and outface the brow
Of bragging horror: so shall inferior eyes,
That borrow their behaviours from the great,
Grow great by your example, and put on
The dauntless spirit of resolution.
Away; and glister like the god of war,
When he intendeth to become the field:
Show boldness, and aspiring confidence.
What, shall they seek the lion in his den,
And fright him there? and make him tremble there?
O, let it not be said!—Forage, and run
To meet displeasure further from the doors;
And grapple with him, ere he come so nigh.

/The Nobles & Knights go up to the back, and confer./

Flourish ready. - L:

K. John. The legate of the pope hath been with me,
And I have made a happy peace with him;
And he hath promis'd to dismiss the powers
Led by the Dauphin.

Bast. O inglorious league!
Shall we, upon the footing of our land,
Send fair-play orders, and make compromise,
Insinuation, parley, and base truce,
To arms invasive? shall a beardless boy,
A cocker'd silken wanton brave our fields,
And flesh his spirit in a warlike soil,
Mocking the air with colours idly spread,
And find no check? Let us, my liege, to arms:
Perchance, the cardinal cannot make your peace;
Or if he do, let it at least be said,
They saw we had a purpose of defence.

K. John. Have thou the ordering of this present time.

Bast. Away then, with good courage; yet, I know,
Our party may well meet a prouder foe. [*Exeunt.*

SCENE II.

A Plain, near St. Edmund's-Bury.

Enter, in arms, LEWIS, SALISBURY, MELUN, PEMBROKE, BIGOT, ~~and Soldiers.~~

Lew. My lord Melun, let this be copied out,
And keep it safe for our remembrance:
Return the precedent[4] to these lords again;
That, ~~having our fair order written down,~~

[4] —— *the* precedent, &c.] i. e. the rough draught of the original treaty between the Dauphin and the English lords.

3.—

Both they, and we, perusing o'er these notes,
May know wherefore we took the sacrament,
And keep our faiths firm and inviolable.
|R| *Sal.* Upon our sides it never shall be broken.
And, noble Dauphin, albeit we swear
A voluntary zeal, and unurg'd faith,
To your proceedings; yet, believe me, prince,
I am not glad that such a sore of time
Should seek a plaster by contemn'd revolt,
And heal the inveterate canker of one wound,
By making many: O, it grieves my soul,
That I must draw this metal from my side
To be a widow-maker; O, and there,
Where honourable rescue, and defence,
Cries out upon the name of Salisbury:
But such is the infection of the time,
That, for the health and physick of our right,
We cannot deal but with the very hand
Of stern injustice and confused wrong.—
And is't not pity, O my grieved friends!
That we, the sons and children of this isle,
Were born to see so sad an hour as this;
Wherein we step after a stranger march
Upon her gentle bosom, and fill up
Her enemies' ranks, (I must withdraw and weep
Upon the spot of this enforced cause,)[5]
To grace the gentry of a land remote,
And follow unacquainted colours here?
What, here?—O nation, that thou could'st remove!
That Neptune's arms, who clippeth thee about,[6]
Would bear thee from the knowledge of thyself,
And grapple thee unto a pagan shore;
Where these two Christian armies might combine

[5] —— *the* spot *of this enforced cause,)*] *Spot* probably means, *stain* or *disgrace*.
[6] —— clippeth *thee about,*] i. e. *embraceth.*

3.—

Pandulph.
2 Knts Templars.
2 Bishops.
2 Monks.
2 Gentlemen.
Bastard.
~~Engh Herald.~~
~~2 Do Knights.~~
Oxford.
Hereford.
Standard Bearer.
(Flag of Truce.)
2 Templar Standards.

Trumpet ready 1.

The blood of malice in a vein of league,
And not to spend it so unneighbourly!
Lew. A noble temper dost thou show in this;
And great affections, wrestling in thy bosom,
Do make an earthquake of nobility.
O, what a noble combat hast thou fought,
Between compulsion and a brave respect![7]
Let me wipe off this honourable dew,
That silverly doth progress on thy cheeks:
My heart hath melted at a lady's tears,
Being an ordinary inundation;
But this effusion of such manly drops,
This shower, blown up by tempest of the soul,
Startles mine eyes, and makes me more amaz'd
Than had I seen the vaulty top of heaven
Figur'd quite o'er with burning meteors.
Lift up thy brow, renowned Salisbury,
And with a great heart heave away this storm:
Commend these waters to those baby eyes,
That never saw the giant world enrag'd;
Nor met with fortune other than at feasts,
Full warm of blood, of mirth, of gossiping.
Come, come; for thou shalt thrust thy hand as deep
Into the purse of rich prosperity,
As Lewis himself:—so, nobles, shall you all,
That knit your sinews to the strength of mine.

Enter Pandulph, attended.

And even there, methinks, an angel spake:
Look, where the holy legate comes apace,

[7] *Between* compulsion *and a brave respect!*] This *compulsion* was the necessity of a reformation in the state; which, according to Salisbury's opinion, (who, in his speech preceding, calls it an *enforced cause,*) could only be procured by foreign arms: and the *brave respect* was the love of his country.

To give us warrant from the hand of heaven;
And on our actions set the name of right,
With holy breath.

Pand. Hail, noble prince of France!
The next is this,—king John hath reconcil'd
Himself to Rome; his spirit is come in,
That so stood out against the holy church,
The great metropolis and see of Rome:
Therefore thy threat'ning colours now wind up,
And tame the savage spirit of wild war;
That, like a lion foster'd up at hand,
It may lie gently at the foot of peace,
And be no further harmful than in show.

Lew. Your grace shall pardon me, I will not back;
I am too high-born to be propertied,
To be a secondary at control,
Or useful serving-man, and instrument,
To any sovereign state throughout the world.
Your breath first kindled the dead coal of wars
Between this chástis'd kingdom and myself,
And brought in matter that should feed this fire;
And now 'tis far too huge to be blown out
With that same weak wind which enkindled it.
You taught me how to know the face of right,
Acquainted me with interest to this land,
Yea, thrust this enterprize into my heart;
And come you now to tell me, John hath made
His peace with Rome? What is that peace to me?
I, by the honour of my marriage-bed,
After young Arthur, claim this land for mine;
And, now it is half-conquer'd, must I back,
Because that John hath made his peace with Rome?
Am I Rome's slave? What penny hath Rome borne,
What men provided, what munition sent,
To underprop this action? is't not I,
That undergo this charge? who else but I,

4.

large Crosses

Enter, L. Card^l^ Pandulph, attended by 2 Bishops, - 2 Gentlemen, - 2 Knts Templars, - 2 Monks, - and 2 Templar Standards, - who go up L. -

4.

K John.
Hubert.
Essex.
1st Eng^h^ Knight.
1st D^o^ Herald.
~~2 Attendants~~. Percy
~~4 Stand^d^ Bearers~~. 2 Pages
(~~With K John's Litter~~)

Trumpet, L.-

/Short, - but loud!/

/Pandulph & Suite, go up, to L./

7

And such as to my claim are liable,
Sweat in this business, and maintain this war?
Have I not heard these islanders shout out,
Vive le roy! as I have bank'd their towns?[8]
Have I not here the best cards for the game,
To win this easy match play'd for a crown?
And shall I now give o'er the yielded set?
No, on my soul, it never shall be said.

Pand. You look but on the outside of this work.

Lew. Outside or inside, I will not return
Till my attempt so much be glorified
As to my ample hope was promised
Before I drew this gallant head of war,[9]
And cull'd these fiery spirits from the world,
To outlook[1] conquest, and to win renown
Even in the jaws of danger and of death.—
[*Trumpet sounds.*
What lusty trumpet thus doth summon us?

Enter the Bastard, *attended,* by Hereford - Oxford - 2 Knights - Herald, and Stand Bearer, /w flag of truce./

Bast. According to the fair play of the world,
Let me have audience; I am sent to speak:—
My holy lord of Milan, from the king
I come, to learn how you have dealt for him;
And, as you answer, I do know the scope
And warrant limited unto my tongue.

Pan. The Dauphin is too wilful-opposite,
And will not temporize with my entreaties;
He flatly says, he'll not lay down his arms.

Bast. By all the blood that ever fury breath'd,

[8] —— *as I have* bank'd their towns?] i. e. sailed along the banks of the river.

[9] —— drew *this gallant head of war,*] i. e. assembled it, drew it out into the field.

[1] —— *outlook* —] i. e. face down, bear down by a show of magnanimity.

The youth says well:—Now hear our English king;
For thus his royalty doth speak in me.
He is prepar'd; and reason too, he should:
This apish and unmannerly approach,
This harness'd masque, and unadvised revel,
This unhair'd sauciness, and boyish troops,
The king doth smile at; and is well prepar'd
To whip this dwarfish war, these pigmy arms,
From out the circle of his territories.
That hand, which had the strength, even at your door,
To cudgel you, and make you take the hatch;[2]
To dive, like buckets, in concealed wells;[3]
To crouch in litter of your stable planks;
To lie, like pawns, lock'd up in chests and trunks;
To hug with swine; to seek sweet safety out
In vaults and prisons; and to thrill, and shake,
Even at the crying of your nation's crow,[4]
Thinking his voice an armed Englishman;—
Shall that victorious hand be feebled here,
That in your chambers gave you chastisement?
No: Know, the gallant monarch is in arms;
And like an eagle o'er his aiery towers,[5]
To souse annoyance that comes near his nest.—
And you degenerate, you ingrate revolts,
You bloody Neroes, ripping up the womb
Of your dear mother England, blush for shame:
For your own ladies, and pale-visag'd maids,
Like Amazons, come tripping after drums;
Their thimbles into armed gauntlets change,

5.-

[2] —— *take the hatch;*] To *take the hatch,* is to *leap the hatch.* To *take a hedge* or a *ditch* is the hunter's phrase.

[3] —— *in* concealed *wells;*] *Concealed wells* are wells in concealed or *obscure* situations; viz. in places *secured from public notice.*

[4] —— *of your nation's crow,*] i. e. at the crowing of a cock; *gallus* meaning both a cock and a Frenchman.

[5] —— *his* aiery *towers,*] An *aiery* is the nest of an eagle.

Flourish ready, 1.-
and
Alarums.- 1.-

5.-

The Cross-Bow, ready for Hubert R-1E.-
and
Couch ready, for K John, R-2E.-

Flourish, L.-

and

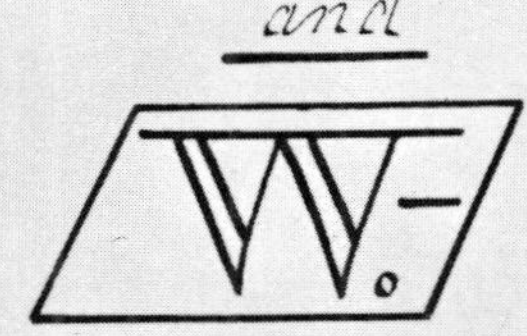

then, Alarums, R. L.

Their neelds to lances,[a] and their gentle hearts
To fierce and bloody inclination.

Lew. There end thy brave, and turn thy face in peace;
We grant, thou canst outscold us: fare thee well;
We hold our time too precious to be spent /going. R.2 E./
With such a brabbler.

Pand. /adv. 2 E./ Give me leave to speak.

Bast. No, I will speak.

Lew. We will attend to neither:—
Strike up the drums; and let the tongue of war
Plead for our interest, and our being here.

Bast. Indeed, your drums, being beaten, will cry out;
And so shall you, being beaten: Do but start
An echo with the clamour of thy drum,
And even at hand a drum is ready brac'd,
That shall reverberate all as loud as thine;
Sound but another, and another shall,
As loud as thine, rattle the welkin's ear,
And mock the deep-mouth'd thunder: for at hand
(Not trusting to this halting legate here,
Whom he hath us'd rather for sport than need,)
Is warlike John; and in his forehead sits
A bare-ribb'd death, whose office is this day
To feast upon whole thousands of the French.

Lew. Strike up our drums, to find this danger out.

Bast. And thou shalt find it, Dauphin, do not doubt.

[Exeunt, Lewis & Fr. Nobles. Salisbury, and Rebel Lords, R.2 Ent.- Bastard, Pand. and their Suites, - L.1 E.-]

[a] *Their neelds to lances,*] i. e. needles.

SCENE III.

The same. A Field of Battle. /Ex./

Alarums. *Enter King* JOHN *and* HUBERT. R.

K. John. How goes the day with us? O, tell me, Hubert.

Hub. Badly, I fear: How fares your majesty?

K. John. This fever, that hath troubled me so long,
Lies heavy on me; O, my heart is sick!

Enter ~~a Messenger~~ 1st English Knight /R./ as from the battle.

Knt.- ~~Mess~~. My lord, your valiant kinsman, Faulconbridge,
Desires your majesty to leave the field;
And send him word by me, which way you go.

K. John. Tell him, toward Swinstead,[7] to the abbey there.

Knt.- ~~Mess~~. Be of good comfort; for the great supply,
That was expected by the Dauphin here,
Are wreck'd three nights ago on Goodwin sands.
This news was brought to Richard[8] but even now:
The French fight coldly, and retire themselves. /Exit, R./

K. John. Ah me! this tyrant fever burns me up,
And will not let me welcome this good news.——
Set on toward Swinstead: to my litter straight;
/going L./ - Weakness possesseth me, and I am faint. [*Exeunt*, L./

[7] —— *Swinstead*,] i. e. *Swineshead*.

[8] —— *Richard* —] *Sir Richard Faulconbridge*;—and yet the King, a little before, (Act III. sc. ii.) calls him by his original name of *Philip*. STEEVENS.

33

Alarums, L.- (swelling and decreasing, through the Scene.)

/ ~~4 Bearers~~, enter, first, with the King's Litter, which is taken across, and off L. - then 2 Attendants, - 1st Engh Herald - K John, supported by Hubert - Esex, last. - All from R. / 2 Pages follow the King

/ The King falls into the arms of Hub' and Esex, and is carried off by them, L.1E.- /

W.-

Alarums continue all thro' next Scene, R- and L.-

SCENE IV.

The same. Another Part of the same.

Enter SALISBURY, PEMBROKE, BIGOT, and Others.

Sal. I did not think the king so stor'd with friends.

Pem. Up once again; put spirit in the French;
If they miscarry, we miscarry too.

Sal. That misbegotten devil, Faulconbridge,
In spite of spite, alone upholds the day.

Pem. They say, king John, sore sick, hath left the field.

Enter MELUN wounded, and led by Soldiers.

Mel. Lead me to the revolts of England here.

Sal. When we were happy we had other names.

Pem. It is the count Melun.

Sal. Wounded to death.

Mel. Fly, noble English, you are bought and sold;
Unthread the rude eye of rebellion,
And welcome home again discarded faith.
Seek out king John, and fall before his feet;
For, if the French be lords of this loud day,
He means[8] to recompense the pains you take,
By cutting off your heads: Thus hath he sworn,
And I with him, and many more with me,
Upon the altar at Saint Edmund's-Bury;
Even on that altar, where we swore to you
Dear amity and everlasting love.

Sal. May this be possible? may this be true?

Mel. Have I not hideous death within my view,

[8] *He means* —] The Frenchman, i. e. Lewis, means, &c.

Retaining but a quantity of life;
Which bleeds away, even as a form of wax
Resolveth from his figure 'gainst the fire?[9]
What in the world should make me now deceive,
Since I must lose the use of all deceit?
Why should I then be false; since it is true
That I must die here, and live hence by truth?
I say again, if Lewis do win the day,
He is forsworn, if e'er those eyes of yours
Behold another day break in the east:
But even this night,—whose black contagious breath
Already smokes about the burning crest
Of the old, feeble, and day-wearied sun,—
Even this ill night, your breathing shall expire;
Paying the fine of rated treachery,[1]
Even with a treacherous fine of all your lives,
If Lewis by your assistance win the day.
Commend me to one Hubert, with your king;
The love of him,—and this respect besides,
For that my grandsire was an Englishman,—
Awakes my conscience to confess all this.
In lieu whereof, I pray you, bear me hence
From forth the noise and rumour of the field;
Where I may think the remnant of my thoughts
In peace, and part this body and my soul
With contemplation and devout desires.

Sal. We do believe thee,—And beshrew my soul
But I do love the favour and the form

[9] —— *even as a* form of wax
Resolveth, *&c.*] This is said in allusion to the images made by witches. Holinshed observes, that it was alledged against dame Eleanor Cobham and her confederates, "that they had devised *an image of wax*, representing the king, which, by their sorcerie, by little and little consumed, intending thereby, in conclusion, to waste and destroy the king's person."

[1] —— rated *treachery*,] i. e. The Dauphin has *rated* your treachery, and set upon it a *fine*, which your lives must pay.

Loud Alarums, L.-

(going to Melun.)

Alarums, - ~~Round~~ 1. -

W. - and -

- Put Lights down.

Prince Henry. Essex. Bedford. 1st & 2nd Knights. (torches) 6 Monks. Mitred Abbot. 4 Herald Bearer (torches) K John.

~~Of this most fair occasion, by the which~~
We will untread the steps of damned flight;
And, like a bated and retired flood,
~~Leaving our rankness and irregular course,~~
~~Stoop low within those bounds we have o'erlook'd,~~
~~And~~ Calmly run on in our obedience,
Even to our ocean, to our great king John.——
My arm shall give thee help to bear thee hence;
For I do see the cruel pangs of death
Right in thine eye.—Away, my friends! ~~New flight;~~
~~And happy newness,[2] that intends old right~~

[*Exeunt, leading off* MELUN, R. - All crowd round, to assist.]

SCENE V.

The same. The French Camp.

Enter LEWIS *and his Train.*

Lew. The sun of heaven, methought, was loath to set;
But stay'd, and made the western welkin blush,
When the English measur'd backward their own ground,
In faint retire: O, bravely came we off,
When with a volley of our needless shot,
After such bloody toil, we bid good night;
And wound our tatter'd colours clearly up,
Last in the field, and almost lords of it!

Enter a Messenger.

Mess. Where is my prince, the Dauphin?
Lew. Here:—What news?

[2] —— *happy* newness, &c.] Happy innovation, that purposed the restoration of the ancient rightful government.

Mess. The count Melun is slain; the English lords,
By his persuasion, are again fallen off:
And your supply, which you have wish'd so long,
Are cast away, and sunk, on Goodwin sands.
Lew. Ah, foul shrewd news!—Beshrew thy very heart!
I did not think to be so sad to-night,
As this hath made me.—Who was he, that said,
King John did fly, an hour or two before
The stumbling night did part our weary powers?
Mess. Whoever spoke it, it is true, my lord.
Lew. Well; keep good quarter,[3] and good care to-night;
The day shall not be up so soon as I,
To try the fair adventure of to-morrow. [*Exeunt.*

SCENE ~~II~~. 5th

/Night./- *An open Place in the Neighbourhood of* Swinstead-Abbey. / Gate of Abbey, -R-1E./ /Gr./

Enter ~~*the Bastard and*~~ HUBERT, ~~*meeting*~~. /R:/ ф

Hub. Who's there? speak, ho! speak quickly, or I shoot.
/with L:/ *Bast.* A friend:—What art thou?
Hub. Of the part of England.
~~*Bast.* Whither dost thou go?~~
~~*Hub.* What's that to thee? Why may not I demand~~
~~Of thine affairs, as well as thou of mine?~~
/Enters, L:/ *Bast.* Hubert, I think.
Hub. Thou hast a perfect thought:
~~I will, upon all hazards, well believe~~

[3] —— *keep good* quarter,] i. e. keep in your allotted posts.

ф / Hubert has a Cross-bow, and walks 3 or 4 times, past the Gate, before he speaks. /

R. M. B.

for Band to come up to K-Ub

~~Thou art my friend, that know'st my tongue so well~~:
Who art thou?

Bast. Who thou wilt: an if thou please,
Thou may'st befriend me so much, as to think
I come one way of the Plantagenets.

Hub. Unkind remembrance! thou, and eyeless night,
Have done me shame:—Brave soldier, pardon me,
That any accent, breaking from thy tongue,
Should 'scape the true acquaintance of mine ear.

Bast. Come, come; sans compliment, what news abroad?

Hub. Why, here walk I, in the black brow of night,
To find you out.

Bast. Brief, then; and what's the news?

Hub. O, my sweet sir, news fitting to the night,
Black, fearful, comfortless, and horrible.

Bast. Show me the very wound of this ill news;
I am no woman, I'll not swoon at it.

Hub. The king, I fear, is poison'd by a monk:*
I left him almost speechless, and broke out
To acquaint you with this evil; ~~that you might~~
~~The better arm you to the sudden~~ time,
~~Than if you had at leisure known of this.~~

Bast. How did he take it? who did taste to him?

Hub. A monk, I tell you; a resolved villain,
Whose bowels suddenly burst out: the king
Yet speaks, and, peradventure, may recover.

* *The king, I fear, is poison'd by a monk:*] Not one of the historians who wrote within sixty years after the death of King John, mentions this very improbable story. The tale is, that a monk, to revenge himself on the king for a saying at which he took offence, poisoned a cup of ale, and having brought it to his majesty, drank some of it himself, to induce the king to taste it, and soon afterwards expired. Thomas Wykes is the first, who relates it in his *Chronicle*, as a *report*. According to the best accounts, John died at Newark, of a fever.

Bast. Who didst thou leave to tend his majesty?
Hub. Why, know you not? the lords are all come back,
And brought prince Henry in their company;
At whose request the king hath pardon'd them,
And they are all about his majesty.
Bast. Withhold thine indignation, mighty heaven,
And tempt us not to bear above our power!——
I'll tell thee, Hubert, half my power this night,
Passing these flats, are taken by the tide,
These Lincoln washes have devoured them;
Myself, well-mounted, hardly have escap'd.
Away, before! conduct me to the king;
I doubt, he will be dead, or ere I come. [*Exeunt,* R./

SCENE VII.

/Moonlight./ – *The Orchard of* Swinstead-Abbey. /5 & 6 Gr./ ϕ

Enter Prince Henry, Salisbury, *and* Bigot. /R.U.E./

P. Hen. It is too late; the life of all his blood
Is touch'd corruptibly; and his pure brain
(~~Which some suppose the soul's frail dwelling-house,~~)
Doth, by the idle comments that it makes,
Foretell the ending of mortality.

Enter Pembroke, /R.U.E./

Pem. His highness yet doth speak; and holds belief, /up, R./
That, being brought into the open air,
It would allay the burning quality
Of that fell poison which assaileth him.
/C./ *P. Hen.* Let him be brought into the orchard here.— /to Bigot, – who Exit's, R.U.E./

Cale McKean

W. – put Blue Mediums on.

ϕ /Entrance to Abbey, – folding gates – R.U.E./

+ Enter Bigod, - 2 Knights, /w torches./ - 6 Monks, carrying a couch, on which K John is lying - a white bandage round his head, - ~~4 Standard bearers, /w torches./~~ - Fitzwalter, - De Warrenne, - Arundel, - De Ros, - Mitred Abbot, - De Clare, - Percy, - and Hereford, following, - R.U.E. - The couch is placed, in front, C. /

Torch Torch Torch Torch

Monk. Monk. Monk. Monk. Monk. Monk. Monk. Monk.

Hereford. Arund. De Ros. Hubert.

Md Abbot. K John. ~~Knight.~~ Norfolk. Bastard P Henry. De War. Knight.

Percy. De Clare

Pemb. Fitzw.

Salisb. Essex.

R. L.

/Disposition, when all on, for end of play./

Doth he still rage? /to Pemb./ [~~Exit Bigot~~.

Pem. He is more patient
Than when you left him; even now he sung.

P. Hen. ~~O vanity of sickness! fierce extremes,~~
~~In their continuance, will not feel themselves.~~
~~Death, having prey'd upon the outward parts,~~
~~Leaves them insensible; and his siege is now~~
~~Against the mind, the which he pricks and wounds~~
~~With many legions of strange fantasies;~~
~~Which, in their throng and press to that last hold,~~
~~Confound themselves. 'Tis strange, that death should sing.~~
I am the cygnet to this pale faint swan,
Who chants a doleful hymn to his own death;
~~And, from the organ-pipe of frailty, sings~~
~~His soul and body to their lasting rest.~~

|R.| - *Sal.* Be of good comfort, prince; for you are born
To set a form upon that indigest
Which he hath left so shapeless and so rude.

~~Re-enter BIGOT and Attendants, who bring in King JOHN in a Chair.~~

K. John. Ay, marry, now my soul hath elbow-room;
It would not out at windows, nor at doors.
There is so hot a summer in my bosom,
That all my bowels crumble up to dust:
I am a scribbled form, drawn with a pen
Upon a parchment; and against this fire
Do I shrink up.

P. Hen. How fares your majesty? /L. of couch./

K. John. Poison'd,—ill fare;—dead, forsook, cast off:
And none of you will bid the winter come,
To thrust his icy fingers in my maw;
Nor let my kingdom's rivers take their course

Through my burn'd bosom; nor entreat the north
To make his bleak winds kiss my parched lips,
And comfort me with cold:—I do not ask you much,
I beg cold comfort; and you are so strait,[5]
And so ingrateful, you deny me that.

P. Hen. O, that there were some virtue in my tears,
That might relieve you!

K. John. The salt in them is hot.—
Within me is a hell; and there the poison
Is, as a fiend, confin'd to tyrannize
On unreprievable condemned blood.

Bast. O, I am scalded with my violent motion,
And spleen of speed to see your majesty.

K. John. O cousin, thou art come to set mine eye:
The tackle of my heart is crack'd and burn'd;
And all the shrouds, wherewith my life should sail,
Are turned to one thread, one little hair:
My heart hath one poor string to stay it by,
Which holds but till thy news be uttered;
And then all this thou see'st, is but a clod,
And module of confounded royalty.[6]

Bast. The Dauphin is preparing hitherward;
Where, heaven he knows, how we shall answer him:
For, in a night, the best part of my power,
As I upon advantage did remove,
Were in the washes, all unwarily,
Devoured by the unexpected flood.[7]

[*The King dies,* falling back, on couch.]

[5] —— *so* strait,] i. e. narrow, avaricious; an unusual sense of the word.

[6] *And* module *of confounded royalty.*] i. e. *model.*

[7] *Were in the washes, all unwarily,* &c.] This untoward accident really happened to King John himself. As he passed from Lynn to Lincolnshire, he lost by an inundation all his treasure, carriages, baggage, and regalia.

∅ /All advance two paces, to couch./

Organ Music ready. R. U. Ent.

Hub. ~~Sal.~~ You breathe these dead news in as dead an ear.—
My liege! my lord!—But now a king,—now thus.
P. Hen. Even so must I run on, and even so stop.
What surety of the world, what hope, what stay,
When this was now a king, and now is clay!
Bast. Art thou gone so? I do but stay behind,
To do the office for thee of revenge;
And then my soul shall wait on thee to heaven,
As it on earth hath been thy servant still.
Now, now, you stars, that move in your right spheres,
Where be your powers? Show now your mended faiths;
And instantly return with me again,
To push destruction, and perpetual shame,
Out of the weak door of our fainting land:
Straight let us seek, or straight we shall be sought;
The Dauphin rages at our very heels.
Sal. It seems, you know not then so much as we:
The cardinal Pandulph is within at rest,
Who half an hour since came from the Dauphin;
And brings from him such offers of our peace
As we with honour and respect may take,
With purpose presently to leave this war.
Bast. He will the rather do it, when he sees
Ourselves well sinewed to our defence.
Sal. Nay, it is in a manner done already;
For many carriages he hath despatch'd
To the seaside, and put his cause and quarrel
To the disposing of the cardinal:
With whom yourself, myself, and other lords,
If you think meet, this afternoon will post
To cónsummate this business happily.
Bast. Let it be so:—And you, my noble prince,
With other princes that may best be spar'd,
Shall wait upon your father's funeral.

Hub. - ~~P. Hen.~~ At Worcester must his body be interr'd;[8]
For so he will'd it.
Bast. Thither shall it then.
And happily may you, sweet prince, put on
The lineal state and glory of the land!
To whom, with all submission, on my knee,
I do bequeath my faithful services
And true subjection everlastingly.
Sal. And the like tender of our love we make,
To rest without a spot for evermore.
P. Hen. I have a kind soul, that would give you thanks,
And knows not how to do it, but with tears.
/All rise./ - *Bast.* O, let us pay the time but needful woe,
Since it hath been beforehand with our griefs.—
This England never did, (nor never shall,)
Lie at the proud foot of a conqueror,
But when it first did help to wound itself.
Now these her princes are come home again,
Come the three corners of the world in arms,
And we shall shock them: Nought shall make us rue,
If England to itself do rest but true. ~~[Exeunt.[9]~~

[8] *At Worcester must his body be interr'd;*] A stone coffin, containing the body of King John, was discovered in the cathedral church of Worcester, July 17, 1797. STEEVENS.

[9] The tragedy of *King John*, though not written with the utmost power of Shakspeare, is varied with a very pleasing interchange of incidents and characters. The lady's grief is very affecting; and the character of the Bastard contains that mixture of greatness and levity which this author delighted to exhibit. JOHNSON.

/All kneel, with Salisbury./

Organ Music, - K.2E.

/The Nobles, &c gather round the body of K John, with varied expressions of grief, as the

Curtain.

descends./

Average Time.
2 Hours & 45 Min's
2. 50

George Ellis.
/T.R.D.L./

5

Tempe 4 E Mulzen Saxon 2 3 - P1

2 Standard 2

3 [illegible] Battle field 1

4 L Battle 1

5 Abbey drop 2 E

6 Abbey drop back 3

Cut Trees [illegible]

Gateway [illegible] 3 8

[illegible] B 3 - 1

8 p 7 -

22

2 Act 24 to 8

5 p 8

3 Act 13 p 8

10 to 9

4 Act 9 -

~~23 to 10~~

15 to 10

15
14 W
29
7 W
32
10 W
35
10 W
27

3 5

12 p 7

27 p 7

2 Act 19 to 8

9 p 8

3 Act 18 p 8

5 to 9

4 Act 5 p 9

20 to 10

5 Act 12 to 9

15
30
37
35